SPARKS

THE LITTLE RED HOUSE

By Norma Jean Sawicki ▲ Illustrated by Toni Goffe

LOTHROP, LEE & SHEPARD BOOKS   NEW YORK

The Little Red House
was inspired by a Mother Goose riddle
in *Popular Rhymes and Nursery Tales*
by James O. Halliwell, John Russell Smith (London) 1849.

First Edition 1 2 3 4 5 6 7 8 9 10

Library of Congress Cataloging in Publication Data

Sawicki, Norma Jean.   The little red house.
Summary: A series of colorful toy houses, each one containing
another slightly smaller, reveals a surprise inside. [1. Color—
Fiction. 2. Toys—Fiction] I. Goffe, Toni. II. Title.
PZ7.S2675Li   1988   [E]   88-2740
ISBN 0-688-07891-5   ISBN 0-688-07892-3 (lib. bdg.)

To
Dorothy Briley,
with love and thanks

—NJS

To
Penelope

—TG

There was a little red house

And in the little red house

There was a little green house

And in the little green house

There was a little yellow house

And in the little yellow house

There was a little brown house

And in the little brown house

There was a little blue house

And in the little blue house

There was a little gray house

And in the little gray house

There was a little purple house

And in the little purple house

There was a little orange house

And in the little orange house

There was a little white house

And in the little white house

EGGS
ON TOP

There was you...

Kiss kiss

INTRODUCTION

Knowing how to properly prepare eggs will make you a better cook. In fact, the one hundred crisp pleats in a chef's tall white toque are said to represent the number of egg dishes in his repertoire.

The magic of egg cookery is one of the great culinary marvels. The egg's versatility as a liquid that readily transforms to a solid with relatively brief exposure to heat makes it an indispensible ingredient in kitchens all over the world.

Yet eggs are also one of the most undervalued foods, their meal-making capabilities often overshadowed by meat outside of the morning hours. Even though eggs are a part of everyone's standard grocery list, sometimes we forget, or don't realize, that sliding a sunny-side up egg onto a plate of steamed rice or sautéed vegetables can transform a side dish into an entrée, with a sauce built right in.

In terms of their nutrient density and their satisfying flavor and richness, eggs are one of nature's most perfect foods. Especially when you consider how economical it is to put this protein on the table. Indeed, even most high-quality, organic, free-range, vegetarian, farm-fresh eggs factor out to no more than sixty cents apiece.

Every Saturday I buy my eggs for the week at the Portland Farmers' Market. I can count on seeing Marvin Kosmal's folding table each week, haphazardly stocked with eggs from the hens, ducks, quail, and geese raised on his Dancing Chicken Farm in La Center, Washington, just across the Columbia River. I can tell from his photo books of his birds and their stomping grounds—a brooder, green pastures, and the nesting coop—that they sure have reason to dance. And proof is in the eggs: They are exceptionally fresh, usually harvested that morning or the day before he brings them to market.

Sometimes out of convenience, I buy eggs at my neighborhood grocery store, and those are quite good, too. With our increasing demand for high-quality eggs from humanely raised hens, the choices at supermarkets are changing for the better.

What's in This Book?

First I divulge classic and clever new techniques for cooking eggs of the chicken, duck, and quail varieties. The second half of the book provides recipes for dishes that are enhanced by eggs, from reimagined classics to new ideas full of worldly flavors, including quick-fix lunches, simple weeknight suppers, and sophisticated weekend brunches and dinners. Armed with this knowledge, a fast, inexpensive meal is always possible, because, heck, who doesn't have an egg on hand?

Eggs to Infinity, and Beyond

I've barely scratched the surface here, because the possibilities are endless. If there's one goal I have for this book, it's to inspire you to search out the freshest, best-quality eggs you can find and to cook them in new ways you never thought possible. Get cracking!

an EGG PRIMER

Is there a protein on Earth that cooks more quickly than an egg? Egg yolks and whites coagulate, or set, at two different temperatures, allowing for fully cooked whites and undercooked yolks. So we are able to cook eggs with two distinctly different textures in one nifty little package. But we must be careful, because excessive coagulation happens fast, pushing moisture from the eggs, which leaves them dry and unremarkable.

The focus of cooking eggs just right is mostly in the doneness of the yolks. Most of us are quite opinionated when it comes to the degree to which we like our egg yolks to be cooked: Some like runny, saucy, totally liquid yolks; some, like me, prefer the yolks to be a bit thickened but still loose and oozy, which I refer to as "molten" yolks in this book. Still others are completely freaked out by a loose yolk and like them cooked until firm, or hard-cooked.

I hope you will see that all these degrees of doneness have their place. Sometimes a liquid yolk is used like a sauce, to moisten the food that the egg is placed atop. But if the eggs are baked in a sauce or liquid or placed over a dish that is already quite moist, the egg yolks are best when they are molten. Because a completely runny yolk would get lost, the slight variation in texture is nice. Firm yolks are great for deviled eggs, or when the egg adorns a cold salad.

CRACKING THE EGG

It's best to gently tap the center of the egg against a hard, flat surface, like a countertop, rather than the edge of a bowl or pan, because it helps to prevent bits of shell from getting into the eggs. And crack the eggs into a small bowl before slipping them into a pan or baking dish. This gives you the chance to inspect for bits of shell, blood spots, or broken yolks. Save eggs with broken yolks for scrambling.

SEPARATING YOLKS FROM WHITES

To separate the yolk from the whites, crack an egg over a small bowl and pass the yolk back and forth between the shell halves, allowing the whites to fall into the bowl. Another method is to crack the egg into your hand and gently pass the yolk back and forth as the whites slip through your fingers. I like that one the best. If you'll be whipping the whites for something like a meringue, be sure not to dribble any of the yolk.

KINDS OF EGGS

Hen eggs are by far the most widely consumed eggs in the world. In the recipes in this book, it is assumed that you will be using an egg from a hen (female chicken), unless another egg is called out. Duck eggs can be used interchangeably with chicken eggs; they just take a little longer to cook. I do hope you will use duck eggs if you can find them at a farmers' market or specialty grocery store. The richness of a duck egg is remarkable when gently cooked, as with poaching and soft cooking in the shell. They add extra va-va-voom to nearly any dish in this book.

Quail eggs are stunning perched atop hors d'oeuvres, and they are quite charming little gems that spruce up most anything from salads to pizza. Every time I cook a quail egg I get giddy with excitement for its adorableness. That miniature, speckled shell with a baby-blue inner lining is almost too pretty to discard. Duck and quail eggs are delicacies in many cultures, and they are becoming increasingly popular on restaurant menus in the United States. So, too, we find them at farmers' markets and specialty grocery stores, especially Asian markets.

Goose eggs are similar to duck eggs, with hard, thick, white shells, but about twice as big. They are equally rich, if not richer, and I love them best when they are soft-cooked in the shell, which takes about 8 minutes using the method in this book (see page 24).

Turkey eggs are about twice the size of hen eggs and come in white shells with brown freckles. They are more similar in flavor to hen eggs than duck or goose but still a little bit more eggy-rich. You'll have to look hard, but you might find turkey and goose eggs at your local farmers' market. A farm specializing in wild game sells them at my market nearly every week.

My hairstylist, Michael, grew up eating scrambled peacock eggs his mother collected from the flock that lived on his family's ranch in Idaho. He says they taste "more eggy, but not gross." In fact, the flavor of most birds' eggs is similar to that of a hen's, but usually a little richer, with a more pronounced eggyness. To the best of my knowledge, eggs from all types of birds are edible, but wild eggs are protected by law. Other types that may be available commercially are eggs of the pigeon, guinea fowl, pheasant, emu, and ostrich, though they'll take some serious hunting down. Fish eggs are edible, too—caviar, roe, bottarga—but I'll save those for another book.

size, quality, and freshness

Hen eggs come in many sizes, depending on the age of the bird that laid them: The larger the egg, the older the hen. They also come in three grades—AA, A, and B—in descending order of quality, but freshness is key. Flavor-wise, a fresh grade A egg will be superior to an aging AA. The recipes in this book were created and tested with farm-fresh grade AA large eggs of the pastured, free-range, or cage-free varieties.

In the United States, eggs produced at farms with more than 3,000 hens are subject to the U.S. Department of Agriculture regulations and inspection. The USDA classifies eggs according to size, based on the weight of the full dozen, so within a carton of eggs you may have some that are a little larger than others, which is also true of eggs purchased from a small farm at the farmers' market. Across the board, eggs are each a little unique and not necessarily uniform in size.

Does Size Matter?

Since this book is not about baking or custard making (which require more precision), the size of the eggs you use in these recipes is of less concern. So unless the recipe specifies a size, any egg will do. Common sense will dictate that if you'd like the egg to be bigger in a particular dish, then you should use larger eggs, but if you'd like a dainty egg presentation, a smaller one is OK. Just adjust the cooking times up or down a little and rely more on the visual cues rather than the time estimates given.

Size	Weight per egg	Weight per dozen
Small	1½ oz/40 g	18 oz/510 g
Medium	1¾ oz/50 g	21 oz/595 g
Large	2 oz/55 g	24 oz/680 g
Extra-Large	2¼ oz/65 g	27 oz/765 g
Jumbo	2½ oz/70 g	30 oz/850 g

What Do Egg Grades Mean?

Quality grades are no indication of freshness, wholesomeness, or nutritional value. They are an indication of quality, or at least the shape the eggs were in immediately after they were laid. As eggs age, the whites and the yolks begin to deteriorate. The ratio of thick white to thin white (see The Architecture of the Egg, page 17) decreases in favor of sthe more watery whites. Yolks lose their rounded appearance and begin to spread wider.

Grade AA means that the yolks are perky and rounded, sitting high on a thick, compact white. When they are fresh, these are the best eggs for poaching and frying. Grade A means that the yolks are a little bit flatter, and the whites a little bit thinner. These are a better buy for scrambling and baking. Grade B eggs are rarely sold at retail. Remember that all eggs begin to flatten and spread as they age, so the best indicator of quality is in their freshness.

Determining Freshness

If you can't recall how many Saturdays ago you bought those eggs at the farmers' market, submerge one in a bowl of water. If it sinks and lies on its side, then it is still fresh. If the wide end points up, it's on its way out but still good for a batch of pancakes. If it floats, um, yeah, that's old.

STORING EGGS

From the time the hen lays the egg, it will be fresh for about a month if it's stored under proper conditions, though I hope you will use it within a week or so for the best flavor and cooking qualities. Store eggs in the refrigerator, below 45°F/7°C, to prevent microbial growth and to keep them fresher longer. Each day that an egg is left at room temperature, it ages the same amount as four days under refrigeration.

Eggshells are porous, thus able to absorb aromas, like chopped onions. Unless your goal is to infuse flavor into the eggs, like the fragrance of a fresh black truffle (see Eggs Baked with Mushrooms, Thyme, and Cream, page 72), store them away from strong-smelling foods in your refrigerator.

You know those egg compartments that most refrigerators have? Well, if yours is on the door to the fridge, don't use it. Agitation causes the whites to loosen and deteriorate. It's best to leave them in the carton they came in, which is designed to keep them fresh.

ARE RAW EGGS SAFE?

When properly handled, eggs pose no greater safety risk than other perishable foods. If a clean, crack-free egg is kept under refrigeration, contamination is an exceptionally rare occurrence. Since salmonella was discovered in the '80s, and even more so in recent years, commercial egg farms have cracked down on potential causes of contamination, and the risk now is considerably lower. To further prevent salmonella, store eggs under refrigeration as soon as you buy them and up until you are about to cook them, wash the shells before cracking, and throw out any eggs with cracks. Cooking eggs all the way through kills salmonella, but I love a saucy yolk, and I'm sure many of you do, too. Most of the recipes in this book are for cooking eggs to the point that the whites are set but the yolks are underdone. It's a minor risk I'm willing to take. If you prefer set yolks, then cook the eggs longer, which, in some instances, may require decreasing the heat to avoid overcooking the whites.

NUTRITION

Eggs are a device for nurturing and developing a living being, each an oval-shaped incubator, a nutrient powerhouse. Eggs are considered to be one of the most fully utilizable sources of protein for the human body, more than other foods like cow's milk, soy milk, meat, and tofu. Eggs contain vitamins A, B6, and B12 and are one of few foods with a natural supply of vitamin D. They also contain selenium, which protects against cancer and heart disease and decreases inflammation, and choline, which improves memory and brain development. If that weren't enough, they house two highly important antioxidants, lutein and zeaxanthin. Eggs are also a source of folate, iron, riboflavin, and zinc, the nutrients that help build muscles, manage weight loss, and promote healthy pregnancies. OK, I'm convinced that they have it wrong; the saying should be "An egg a day keeps the doctor away."

Nutritionists in decades past claimed that eggs were the great causes of heart disease via high cholesterol. The thinking was that egg yolks contain cholesterol, cholesterol clogs arteries, and clogged arteries cause heart attacks. Many avoided the yolks (which, unfortunately for them, contain most of the nutrients in an egg) or turned to egg substitutes. (Can a processed food really be better?)

After decades of research, scientists have found that an egg a day is overwhelmingly good for us, with benefits that far outweigh the potential negative effects of 5 grams of fat per 55-gram egg. The fact is that saturated fat is the culprit for raising cholesterol, and egg yolks contain mostly unsaturated fats. Moreover, the USDA recently reviewed egg nutrient data and found that eggs actually contain about 12 percent less cholesterol than was previously thought. And eggs are practically a diet food, with just 70 calories per large egg but a whopping 7 grams of protein. For healthy people, there is no evidence to suggest that eating an egg yolk every day will result in high cholesterol or cardiovascular disease. In the USDA's current version of its dietary guidelines, eggs are listed in the chapter titled "Foods and Nutrients to Increase." Still, an egg contains roughly two-thirds of the recommended 300-milligram limit for daily cholesterol intake, so people with high cholesterol should consult their doctor about egg consumption before taking on an egg-a-day diet.

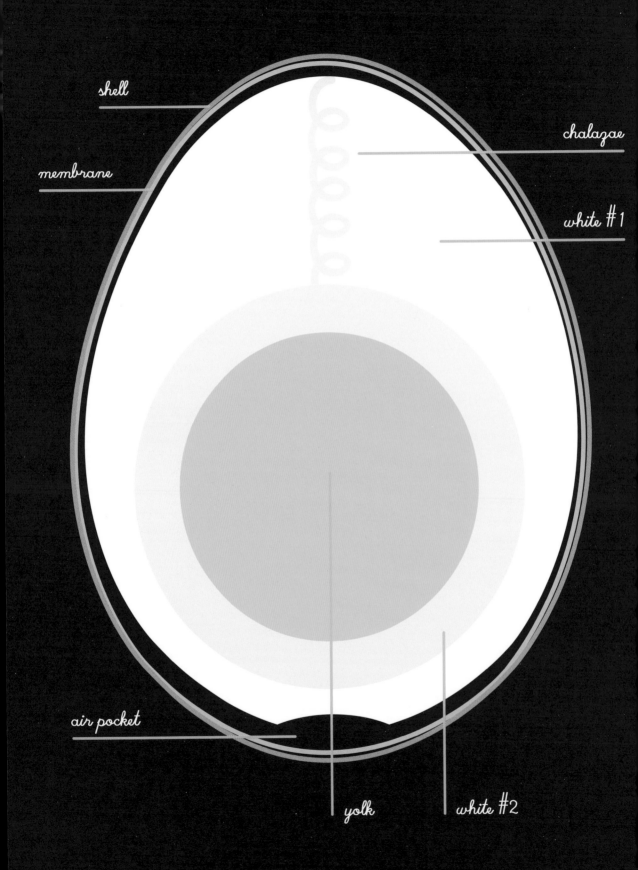

shell

membrane

chalazae

white #1

air pocket

yolk

white #2

the ARCHITECTURE of the EGG

Eggs are made up of various parts that add up to one transcendent food. About a quarter of the hen's daily energy goes to the creation of an egg. She will produce eight times her body weight in eggs in her lifetime, typically at least 250 eggs per year over a two-year span. Here's what all that hard work is for.

THE SHELL: WHITE VS. BROWN

Whether you buy white or brown eggs does not matter in terms of flavor, nutrition, or quality; it's a mere reflection of the breed of hen. Typically, white hens lay white eggs, and brown hens lay brown eggs. The most common breed in America is the White Leghorn. Brown eggs, which are more popular in the Northeastern part of the country, most commonly come from Rhode Island Reds. If you come across a pretty greenish-blue egg, that's from a rarer breed, the Chilean Araucana. You may notice that shells of smaller eggs are thicker than those of larger ones, because hens always produce the same amount of calcium carbonate—the main ingredient in an eggshell—regardless of their size. Though the shell is a neat little package, it is porous, so be aware that air and moisture can pass through.

THE SHELL MEMBRANES: THE GREAT PROTECTORS

That plasticky film beneath the shell of a hard-cooked egg is there for its protection. It is actually two separate membranes, which act as barriers to keep out bacteria and other potential invaders.

THE AIR POCKET: AN INDICATOR OF FRESHNESS

Between the shell membranes, a little pocket of air forms at the wide end of an egg as its contents cool after it's laid. It is a helpful place to start peeling soft- and hard-cooked eggs.

17

As an egg ages, the air pocket becomes larger as moisture escapes through the permeable shell, so a large air pocket means the egg is not so fresh.

THE WHITES: YES, THERE ARE TWO

The whites, or albumen, make up about two-thirds of the edible portion of the egg for a volume of about 2 tablespoons per large egg. I say "whites" because there are actually two distinctly different textures, for lack of a better word, that make up the transparent part of the uncooked egg: a thicker portion surrounding the yolk and a thinner portion around the outside. Quality eggs are marked by a more prominent thick white, which will break down over time into the thinner version. That's about 90 percent water and the rest mostly protein, though there is a trace amount of sugar (in the form of glucose), which is why eggs cooked over high heat will crisp and brown. Whites transform from a translucent liquid to a white solid between 145 and 150°F/ 63 and 65°C, conveniently just before the yolks begin to solidify.

THE YOLK: A GOLDEN ORB OF GOODNESS

The yolk makes up one-third of the edible portion of the egg, with a volume of 1 tablespoon per large egg. The color of the yolk is an indication of what the hen was eating before laying it. Corn and alfalfa contribute to a deeper yellow hue, as do marigold petals, which some farms add to the feed for purely aesthetic reasons. Yolks react to heat a little more slowly than whites: They firm up between 150 and 158°F/65 and 70°C, allowing us to have gloriously runny yolks in unison with pleasantly set whites. I cringe at the thought of an egg-white omelet, because the yolk is the best part of the egg in terms of nutrition, flavor, texture, and visual appeal.

THE CHALAZAE: CHALA-WHAT?

Two curlicue cords of egg white anchor the yolk in the center of the egg. The more distinguished the chalazae (kuh-LEY-zuh), the fresher the egg. Don't worry, they are absolutely edible, and you don't even notice them when the egg is cooked.

a LEXICON of EGG Labels

Approaching the refrigerated wall of egg options at the grocery store can be perplexing. Should you buy the brown or white, local or humane, organic or vegetarian, cage-free or free-range? It can become a guilt-laden decision. Eek! A bit heavy when all you really want to do is make an omelet. While many labels give good guidance, the marketing of eggs has become unnecessarily overwhelming because some of the terms are nothing to cluck about. Here's what it all means.

Cage-Free:
This can include eggs from free-range, free-roaming, barn-roaming, and barn-raised hens that are not confined to battery cages, but it does not necessarily mean that they have access to the outdoors. Most are indoor facilities, but they do have slightly more natural conditions, like perches and nesting and floor space.

Free-Range:
Hens that have access to the outdoors for at least part of the day, perches, and nesting and floor space lay these eggs. But the notion of *free range* encompasses a broader range of conditions than it sounds and it may not mean that the hens can truly roam freely in and out of doors. With the increased risk associated with this type of farming comes elevated prices, but they are well worth the cost.

Gluten-Free:
This one is funny. All eggs are gluten-free; even if the hen is fed grains containing gluten, she won't pass it on to the egg.

Hormone-Free:
By law, the egg industry does not use hormones, so this is just marketing mumbo jumbo.

Humane:
This is not a USDA label, but other reputable organizations, such as Humane Farm Animal Care, offer certification to worthy farms raising chickens under humane conditions. This usually means that they are cage-free, have free access to fresh feed and water, can fully spread their wings, and have the opportunity to exhibit other natural behaviors.

Natural:
The term *natural* means nothing really. The USDA deems all eggs in their shell natural.

Nutrient-Enhanced Eggs:
These are eggs laid by hens on a gourmet diet of things like flaxseed, fish oils, or algae, which increase the eggs' nutrient density.

Omega-3:
All eggs naturally contain an average of 30 milligrams of omega-3 fatty acids, but some hens are fed a diet rich in omega-3s to increase their content to 100 to 600 milligrams per egg.

Organic:
To receive this coveted label, the hens have to both be raised on a diet of certified organic feed and live in a cage-free environment with access to the outdoors, which can mean a screened-in porch.

Pasteurized:
These are heat-treated to just below the coagulation point in order to kill pathogens. If you're worried about salmonella poisoning, or if you are pregnant or feeding children, elderly people, or anyone else with a weakened immune system, use these in raw and undercooked egg preparations.

Pastured:
You'll rarely see this claim on an egg carton, because hens raised on an open pasture, eating a natural diet of insects and plants, are relatively rare. Few farms take on the labor-intensive raising of pastured hens. Those that do usually have a flock far below the 3,000-hen limit for USDA inspection, so the term is not regulated. These eggs are worth searching out and worth the five to eight dollars per dozen. Look for them at farmers' markets, local specialty food stores, and co-ops.

Vegetarian:
Though not a natural diet for hens (they like bugs!), vegetarian-fed eggs are gaining market share because of our fear of chickens being fed chicken, which is a shady practice that does happen, unfortunately. This is all the more reason to know the farm from which you buy your eggs.

Vitamin E:
Eggs also contain a bit of this naturally, but not enough to be a significant source, so some hens are fed a diet rich in vitamin E. To receive this label, the eggs must provide at least 10 percent of the daily recommended value of vitamin E.

PART I.
LET'S GET CRACK-ING

EGGS

COOKED in their Shells

Eggs are cooked in their shells to produce hard- or soft-cooked eggs and coddled eggs, which vary by the degree of doneness in both the white and the yolk. They may be peeled, cracked open, and eaten directly from the shell, or, in the case of coddled eggs, poured from it.

"Boiled" eggs are one of the first things that most people learn to cook, yet there seems to be much mystery surrounding this fundamental technique. The fact is that you really don't want to boil eggs but cook them at a bare simmer to keep the whites soft and tender and keep the shells from cracking against each other.

There's certainly more than one way to simmer eggs in their shells. Some begin with the eggs in cold water and slowly bring the water up to a simmer and keep it there until the eggs are cooked. Others take the pot off the heat at the moment that a few large bubbles break the surface, and let the eggs steep in the hot water. The method that I prefer, which is also the one that many restaurant chefs use, is to sink the eggs into already-boiling water.

I think this is the best method for a few reasons. For one thing, there's more control over the amount of time that the eggs are cooking. With the cold-water methods, there are many variables that affect the amount of time the eggs are exposed to heat, and, consequently, how done the yolks will be. And a minute or two makes a significant difference in the doneness of the eggs. Also, you have to watch the water carefully, waiting for it to come to a simmer before starting your timer, for much longer than I care to watch water heat. With the boiling-water method, you know the precise time the eggs hit the hot water, and that's when you start your timer. But the main reason why I prefer the boiling-water method is because it is miraculous how easy the eggs are to peel after cooking. Sometimes the shells are so loose they practically fall off in my hand!

Eggs are easier to peel when they are older because they become less acidic and more alkaline. The higher acidity of fresh eggs causes the whites to cling to the shell, and over time, as the pH rises, they lose their grip. For easier peeling, it's commonly recommended that we buy our eggs fresh from the farm and put them in the back of the fridge for a week or two until they're a little bit older. But doesn't that defeat the point of buying farm-fresh eggs? Luckily and for some unknown reason, with the boiling-water method, even the freshest of fresh eggs peels with ease.

Keys to cooking eggs in their shells:

• *Start with eggs at room temperature, to ensure the timing will be right and to prevent the shells from breaking when they hit the hot water. Take them out of the refrigerator at least an hour before cooking for the best results.*

• *Choose eggs that are free of cracks. Eggs that have even hairline cracks in their shells will inevitably crack open and seep out some of their whites while cooking. Besides the fact that they aren't pretty, they may not be safe to eat, so discard them. If you need an exact number of perfectly cooked eggs for a recipe, cook a couple of extra just in case you get a few leakers.*

• *When the timer goes off, plunge the eggs into a big bowl of ice water to stop the cooking. It cools the eggs quickly so that you can get to peeling and eating, but more important, it prevents that nasty green ring from appearing around the yolk.*

• *Hard-cooked eggs are easiest to peel when they are still warm, but it's best to peel soft-cooked eggs when they are completely cold because the whites will be firmer. Peel the eggs under cold running water to wash away the shell as you peel and to help get under the shell membrane, that plasticky thin coating between the shell and the white. Start peeling from the air pocket at the wider end of the egg and work your way to the tip.*

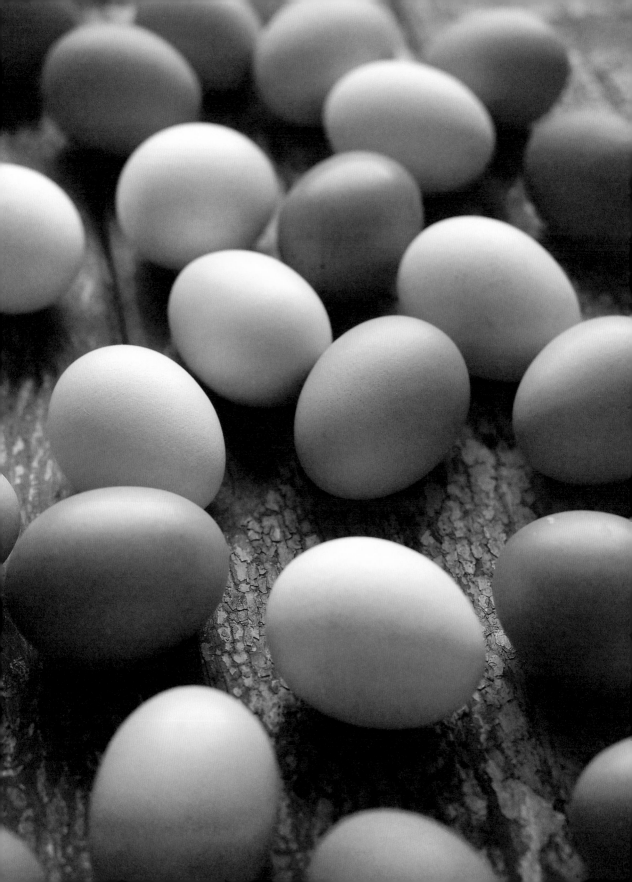

SIMMERED EGGS

PREPARATION

Select a pot that's just large enough to comfortably accommodate the number of eggs you'd like to cook. A 2-qt/2-L saucepan is a good size for six eggs, or a 4-qt/3.8-L pot for twelve. Fill it with 3 in/7.5 cm of water and bring it to a boil over high heat. Add a few big pinches of salt. Reduce the heat to medium and wait for the rapid boil to calm to gentle bubbles, then lower the eggs into the water using a slotted spoon or a large-mesh skimmer. Set a timer according to the doneness you want (see Cooking Times and Characteristics at right), and check the eggs occasionally to be sure they stay at a gentle simmer with just a few soft bubbles breaking the surface at any given moment, adjusting the heat up or down as needed. When the timer goes off, immediately lift the eggs from the water and transfer them to a bowl of ice water to stop cooking. When they are completely chilled, drain and dry the eggs and store them in the refrigerator in their shells for up to 1 week. Or wait until the eggs are cool enough to handle and peel and eat them right away.

To peel hard-cooked eggs (those cooked 8 minutes or more), one by one, tap and roll them against the countertop, applying gentle pressure, making tiny cracks all over like a mosaic. This technique is a little too aggressive for soft-cooked eggs (those cooked 7 minutes or fewer) with delicate whites, so cradle those in your hand and gently tap the shells with the back of a spoon to make the tiny cracks.

Working under cool, trickling water, start peeling at the thickest end of the egg, using the empty air pocket to get a grip on the shell. Get under the membrane and peel with the side of your thumb, working around the egg. When you get the hang of it, you'll be able to strip off the shell like the peel of an apple, in one long continuous coil. The bottom third, toward the tip, might just come off in one big sheath.

COOKING TIMES AND CHARACTERISTICS

These times are for farm-fresh, large, grade AA eggs at room temperature. For older eggs, the following times may need to be reduced slightly since the ratio of thin to thick whites will be increased so they will cook a little faster. For extra-large or duck eggs, the times should be increased by about 1 minute. For quail eggs, simmer 2 minutes for molten yolks, 2½ for soft-cooked, 3 for hard-cooked with creamy yolks, and 3½ for fully set yolks.

3-Minute Eggs

Liquid yolks surrounded by creamy whites that are barely congealed and milky around the yolk (not firm enough to peel). These are the eggs to set in an eggcup. Slice just enough off the top to dig in with a small spoon or a strip of toasted bread, and eat the egg directly from the shell.

4-Minute Eggs

Runny, liquid yolks surrounded by loose and creamy inner whites. The outer whites are so soft and supple that peeling takes an extra-gentle touch.

5-Minute Eggs

Yolks are just beginning to thicken but still flowing. I call them "molten" yolks. Whites are extremely tender, so peel gingerly. The French refer to these as *mollet* eggs. They can be used interchangeably with poached eggs.

6-Minute Eggs

Creamy, thickened yolks with barely molten centers. Whites are very tender but a little easier to peel. This is the classic soft-cooked egg, good for halving to top salads or slip into soups.

7-Minute Eggs

Thickened yolks are barely set, extremely moist, creamy, and golden. Whites are tender and peel rather easily.

8-Minute Eggs

Yolks are set but moist, creamy, and golden with just the edges turned light yellow. Whites are firm but tender and easy to peel. Some prefer these to traditional hard-cooked eggs because of their richer yolks.

9- to 12-Minute Eggs

Set yolks with a ring of powdery light-yellow creeping in on the creamy, golden centers. By 12 minutes they are nearly fully set. Whites are firm though tender.

13-Minute Eggs

Yolks are a powdery pale yellow all the way through. Both yolks and whites are fully set but still tender and not dry. This is the classic hard-cooked egg for deviling or chopping into egg salad.

15-Minute Eggs

The egg is on its way to overcooked, with a bare hint of greenish-gray beginning to appear around the outside of the dry yolk.

3-Minute Egg

4-Minute Egg

5-Minute Egg

6-Minute Egg

7-Minute Egg

8-Minute Egg

9- to 12-Minute Egg

13-Minute Egg

15-Minute Egg

GRATED EGGS

Grated hard-cooked eggs add texture and richness to cooked vegetables and salads. They are a sublime idea when you're looking for something to add a bit of rich balance to crisp vegetables dressed in tart vinaigrette, which gives a result similar to adding crumbled cheese. An especially good example is asparagus mimosa (mimosa is a fancier word for "grated eggs"), a dish of steamed or roasted asparagus tossed in a simple vinaigrette and topped with a generous showering of grated egg.

on either the large or small holes of a box grater, depending on the texture you're going for. I typically use the larger holes for a chunkier texture in rustic dishes and save finely grated eggs for more delicate, refined applications. After grating, mix the whites and yolks together. Alternatively, grate only the yolks for an extra-rich rendition.

You can also finely chop the egg with a knife, which yields a similar effect, but slightly different texture.

PREPARATION

Begin with as many peeled 13-minute eggs (see page 28) as you'd like to grate. Because the white and yolk have different textures, it is best to separate them before grating (for ease, you could grate the whole egg, but the texture will be a little inconsistent). To separate the white and yolk, cut a hard-cooked egg in half as you would an avocado, treating the yolk as if it's the pit; the goal is to keep the yolk whole. Then simply pull the 2 halves of the white away from the yolk (they should easily separate). Grate the white and yolk separately

CODDLED EGGS

This is the most underutilized method of cooking eggs. I'm not talking about cooking eggs in those cute little lidded dishes here. (Though those are nice too; see Foolproof Poached Eggs, page 44, for a similar technique.) This technique is simpler, but the resulting texture is transcendent. These coddled eggs are barely cooked in their shells by submerging them in near-boiling water so that the whites hardly get the chance to set and the yolks remain completely liquid. These are the ideal eggs to drop into a brothy soup, like ramen. They melt away, thickening and enriching the hot broth.

PREPARATION

Put as many room-temperature eggs as you'd like to cook in a tall heat-proof vessel, such as a measuring cup or a narrow pitcher. Pour in at least 1 cup/240 ml of boiling water per egg, so that the eggs are completely submerged, and set a timer for 8 minutes. When the timer goes off, drain the eggs and quickly plunge them into a bowl of ice water to stop the cooking. If you'll be serving them later, cool them completely. If you're serving them immediately, leave them in the ice water for only 1 or 2 minutes, just until they're cool enough to touch.

To peel, lightly tap the wide end of the egg on the countertop to crack around the air pocket. Holding the egg with the wide end pointing up, start peeling around the air pocket, being sure to get under the shell membrane, just to create an opening that's wide enough for the egg to slip through. Then pour the egg from the shell into the dish that it is destined for, which is probably a hot bowl of soup. Be sure that the broth is piping hot, reheating the egg on contact.

Japanese soy sauce eggs (SHOYU TAMAGO)

makes 4 eggs

In Japan, hard-cooked eggs are braised in soy sauce to impart a salty, savory flavor. The process dyes the eggs a striking shade of brown. Though hard-cooked eggs are traditional and make a brilliant snack by themselves, I like to use eggs with molten yolks to top Japanese-inspired dishes, like Miso-Creamed Kale and Mushrooms with Soy Sauce Eggs (page 166), but the choice is yours.

INGREDIENTS

¼ cup/60 ml Japanese soy sauce (shoyu), preferably tamari

Four 5- to 13-Minute Eggs (see page 28), cold and peeled

PREPARATION

Bring the soy sauce to a boil in a small saucepan over medium-high heat and cook until slightly thickened, about 2 minutes. Add the eggs and simmer, occasionally swirling the pan and turning the eggs in the thickening soy sauce with a wooden spoon and a gentle touch. Continue until the soy sauce is mostly evaporated and the eggs are dyed coffee brown. Remove the pan from the heat and transfer the eggs to a plate to cool, or serve them hot. The color doesn't stay nice for long, so make them within a few hours of when they will be eaten.

chinese tea eggs

makes 6 eggs

Beautiful mosaic eggs are easier to make than you might think. This is the one instance in this book that a grayish-green ring around the yolk is OK and expected. You see, these Chinese delicacies are boiled in a sultry brew of tea, spices, soy, and sugar for at least a half hour (some recipes say 3 hours!) to stain the eggs with color and flavor. They are quite stunning when presented at the table, piled in a pretty bowl like antique ornaments in a museum. But to perch one atop the Garlic-Scallion Noodles (page 199) is the real masterpiece.

INGREDIENTS

Six 8-Minute Eggs (see page 28), cold but unpeeled

¼ cup/10 g loose-leaf black tea, such as Lapsang Souchong (smoky) or Earl Grey (citrusy)

¼ cup/60 ml soy sauce

2 tbsp light or dark brown sugar

1 star anise pod

1 cinnamon stick

1 tsp peppercorns

1½ cups/360 ml water

PREPARATION

One by one, cradle the eggs in your palm and use the back of a spoon to tap a web of fine cracks in the shells, like a mosaic. You need to crack firmly enough to penetrate the membrane between the shell and egg white, but not so hard that the shell flakes away. If a piece of shell falls off here and there, the contrast will be lovely.

Put the eggs in a 1½-qt/1.4-L saucepan with the tea, soy sauce, sugar, star anise, cinnamon, peppercorns, and water and bring to a boil over high heat. Reduce the heat to low, cover the pot, and cook for 30 minutes to dye the eggs. Gently stir the eggs in the tea a few times to be sure they are cooking and dyeing evenly. Adjust the heat as needed to maintain a low simmer. It may be necessary to set the pan slightly off the burner to keep the heat low enough.

Remove the pot from the heat, uncover, and let the eggs cool in the tea until they reach room temperature. Transfer the eggs and tea to a storage container and refrigerate to cool completely, or peel and eat right away. For darker marbling, leave the eggs in the tea overnight; the longer they soak, the deeper the flavor and color. The unpeeled eggs will keep for a few days, out of the tea, refrigerated in a covered container.

PERFECTLY POACHED *eggs*

Poaching, though feared by many and seemingly decadent, is actually one of the healthiest, purest, and simplest ways to cook an egg. All it takes is the proper technique and a bit of practice, and soon you'll be poaching like a pro.

The goal with poaching eggs is to cook them just until that perfect point when the white is set but the yolk isn't. Therefore, it is imperative that the whites completely encase the yolk. This recipe shows you a nifty trick for achieving that, but it is also essential that the eggs be super-fresh.

An acidic liquid (e.g., vinegar) helps to coagulate the white quickly when the egg is slipped into the water, also limiting the amount of stringy strands of thin white that separate from the egg. Most recipes recommend that you add vinegar to the pot of simmering water, but I find it more effective to "marinate" the raw eggs in the vinegar before dropping them in the water.

An age-old method of poaching that is often overlooked is to poach eggs in flavorful liquids, like milk or wine, imparting both flavor and color. Eggs can even be poached directly in a brothy soup or simmered in a hearty stew.

KEYS TO PERFECTLY POACHING EGGS:

- *Cold eggs produce the best results because they are stiff and hold together better in a neat little ball.*

- *The eggs should be extremely fresh, because older eggs have a higher ratio of thin white to thick white, and the thin white is what causes the stringy flyaways. Older eggs aren't ideal for poaching. If they aren't fresh from the farm within a day or two, you can strain away the thin white through a mesh strainer to limit the amount of flyaways, which in turn increases the yolk-to-white ratio—a desirable effect if you ask me. This isn't necessary if your eggs are indeed exceptionally fresh from the farm or perhaps your own backyard.*

- *Creating a whirlpool in the simmering water, and slipping an egg into the center of the vortex, forces the white to wrap around the yolk in a perfect oval. To do this the eggs must be poached individually, then cooled in an ice bath to stop them from overcooking while you poach the remaining eggs. Then all of the eggs are reheated together in barely simmering water just before serving. This makes them easy to prepare ahead of time because all of the poached eggs can be refrigerated, in the ice bath, for up to 2 days before reheating and serving.*

- *Duck and quail eggs are marvelous when poached. Cook them just the same as chicken eggs, but increase the simmering time to 3 to 3½ minutes for duck eggs, and decrease it to about 30 seconds for quail eggs. Also, quail eggs require only ¼ tsp of vinegar for marinating.*

QUINTESSENTIAL POACHED EGGS

makes 4 eggs

To achieve a perfectly oval, pillowy poached egg, it's essential that the eggs be extremely fresh. When you master this technique you'll be staying in for Sunday eggs benedict, and placing them atop nearly anything throughout the week for a quick lunch or dinner.

INGREDIENTS

4 tsp distilled or white wine vinegar
4 farm-fresh eggs, cold
Salt and freshly ground pepper (optional)

PREPARATION

Fill a medium saucepan with at least 3 in/7.5 cm of water and bring it to a boil over high heat. Reduce the heat to medium-high to maintain a steady simmer. Have ready four small bowls.

If the eggs are not extremely fresh, strain away the thin whites: One at a time, crack the eggs into a slotted spoon or large-mesh strainer set over a bowl to strain away the thin white (don't use a fine-mesh strainer, or the thin whites won't be able to filter through).

Carefully slip an egg into each of the bowls. Pour 1 tsp of the vinegar over one of the eggs, and marinate it for about 5 minutes before poaching. Wait to add 1 tsp of vinegar to each of the remaining eggs until about 5 minutes before they will be poached. Fill a large bowl with ice water and set it next to the stove.

Using a slotted spoon, vigorously swirl the simmering water until a whirlpool forms in the center. Lower the bowl with the marinated egg down to the center of the swirling water so that the lip of the bowl touches the water, and let the egg and the vinegar slip into the vortex. Continue to gently swirl the water around the egg until it returns to a simmer. The egg white should wrap tightly around the yolk, forming a pillowy oval shape. As soon as the water returns to a simmer, reduce the heat to medium and simmer the egg for 2 to 2½ minutes for medium and large eggs, or 3 to 3½ minutes for extra-large, jumbo, or duck eggs. To see if it's done, lift the egg from the water with a slotted spoon and gently feel around the edges of the yolk: The yolk should be jiggly and the white should feel set yet tender. Transfer the poached egg to the bowl of ice water to stop the cooking.

Repeat the poaching process with the remaining eggs, skimming away any white foam as needed. The eggs can be left in the ice water and refrigerated for up to 2 days before reheating and serving.

To serve, return all the eggs at once to a pot of barely simmering water to warm through, about 1 minute. Remove them with a slotted spoon and blot on a kitchen towel. Use kitchen shears to trim away any stray strands of egg white. Season with salt and pepper, if desired, and serve immediately.

continued

coatings and toppings

After poaching, roll the eggs in delicate herbs, seeds, or spices for flavor, texture, and visual appeal. Try these:

· Minced or very finely sliced fresh herbs, such as parsley, chives, basil, mint, dill, tarragon, or fennel fronds

· Poppy seeds

· Freshly cracked pink peppercorns

· Black sesame seeds

· Togarashi

· Dukkah (see page 71)

· Seasoned bread crumbs lightly toasted in olive oil

· Finely ground toasted nuts, like pistachios or hazelnuts

· Crushed salt-and-vinegar potato chips

POACHED EGGS FOR A CROWD

PREPARATION

To poach more than four eggs, follow the preceding directions for Quintessential Poached Eggs, but skip the vortex method; it's too time-consuming and the water will become too vinegary. The eggs will be just as good if you poach them together, using a large, wide pot that will comfortably hold the number of eggs you want to poach. Fill it with at least 3 in/7.5 cm of water, preferably more. The deeper the water, the more rounded the eggs will be, because as they fall through the water the whites will encircle the yolk. Also, the vinegar will be more diluted in a larger pot of water.

wine-poached eggs

makes 4 eggs

A bastion of Burgundian cuisine, eggs poached in red wine are the main ingredient in the classic dish Oeufs en Meurette (see page 93). I find that the dark, inky reds of the south of France dye the eggs a more appetizing shade of purple. Either way, use a wine that is fit for drinking but certainly not your finest bottle.

INGREDIENTS

One 750-ml bottle French red wine

4 farm-fresh eggs, cold (see Cook's Note)

PREPARATION

Bring the wine to a simmer over medium heat in a 4-qt/3.8-L saucepan. Crack an egg into each of four separate bowls. One at a time, lower the bowls to the surface of the simmering wine and let the egg slip out. Adjust the heat as needed to maintain a very low simmer with just a few gentle bubbles breaking the surface, but enough to keep the eggs from resting on the bottom of the pot.

Poach the eggs 2 to 3 minutes, depending on their size. To see if they're done, lift an egg from the milk with a slotted spoon and gently feel around the edges of the yolk: The yolk should be jiggly and the white should feel set yet tender. Strain the eggs from the wine using the slotted spoon, and place them onto the dish they are destined for, or transfer them to a bowl of ice water to stop the cooking if you plan to serve them later. They can be kept refrigerated in the ice water for up to 1 day. To serve, reheat the eggs in a pot of barely simmering water just to warm through, about 1 minute.

cook's note: *To poach more than 4 eggs, cook them in batches using the same wine.*

MILK-POACHED EGGS

makes 2 eggs

On a cold winter morning, I like these simply served on a slice of buttered toast. It's nice to spoon a little of the milk over the bread, too. But who can argue with milky-soft eggs on a bowl of steaming savory porridge, as in Pimento Cheese Grits with Greens and Milk-Poached Eggs (page 172)?

INGREDIENTS

1 cup/240 ml milk

Salt

2 farm-fresh eggs, cold

PREPARATION

Warm the milk with a pinch of salt in a small saucepan over medium-high heat. (Don't be tempted to add vinegar to the eggs, as you would for water poaching, because it will cause the milk to curdle.) Crack the eggs into separate small bowls. When the milk is foamy on top and you can see little bubbles starting to break the surface, gently slip the eggs in, one by one, on opposite sides of the pan. If the yolks aren't quite submerged, use a spoon to delicately baste them with the hot milk. Adjust the heat as needed to keep the milk from boiling; it should be steaming and foamy, but not bubbling.

Poach the eggs 2 to 3 minutes, depending on their size. To see if they're done, lift an egg from the milk with a slotted spoon and gently feel around the edges of the yolk: The yolk should be jiggly and the white should feel set yet tender. Strain the eggs from the milk using the slotted spoon, and place them onto the dish they are destined for.

FOOLPROOF POACHED EGGS

makes 4 eggs

Those of you who struggle with egg poaching will love this one. This is a technique from Spanish chef Juan Mari Arzak, in which the egg is tied up in a sheet of plastic wrap, like a little purse, and cooked in simmering water. After poaching, the plastic is snipped and the eggs emerge with a frilly, flowery, ruffly appearance that is devilishly impressive and so simple to get right.

The plastic wrap is slicked with olive oil, butter, duck fat, or any flavorful fat you'd like and placed in a little bowl to clutch the raw egg before tying. Consider this coating of fat a blank canvas to add decorative garnishes to the egg, like fresh herb sprigs, poppy seeds, or cracked peppercorns. When the plastic is removed after poaching, the embellishments will be cooked onto the surface of the egg.

My second favorite thing about these eggs, besides their charming appearance, is that they are far easier to make for a large group than traditional poached eggs. You can poach as many as you'd like all at once in a big pot, just be sure the eggs have room to float about freely. The egg purses can even be assembled in advance and kept in the refrigerator for a day before poaching, which also infuses the flavor of the fat into the egg before cooking. Then poach them right before you plan to eat because they won't hold well after cooking.

INGREDIENTS

4 farm-fresh eggs

Olive oil, melted butter, or other fat, for brushing

3 tbsp fresh tender herbs (chopped or whole), poppy seeds, freshly ground pepper, or other spices (optional)

PREPARATION

For each egg, cut out two 6-in/15-cm squares of plastic wrap and stack one on top of the other, laying them out flat on the countertop. Brush the top layer of plastic with a very light coating of fat, in a circle that's just big enough for an egg. Sprinkle with some of the chopped herbs, seeds, pepper, or other spices, or fan out whole tender herb sprigs (like dill or tarragon) here and there, if using. Gently press them in to stick. Line a teacup or small bowl with the two squares of plastic wrap, herb-side up, and crack an egg into it. Gather the edges of the plastic wrap and twist it as close to the egg as possible, then tie it with kitchen twine. Repeat to tie up each egg.

Choose a pot that will comfortably fit all the eggs and fill it with about 3 in/7.5 cm of water. Bring to a boil, then reduce the heat until the water is at a very gentle simmer. Lower in the eggs and cook for 4 to 5 minutes, until the white is set and the yolk is still runny. It can be difficult to judge the doneness of the whites right around the yolk, so if a little creamy white encircling the yolk bothers you, keep them in for the full 5 minutes. Remove the eggs from the water and snip the twine to free the eggs. Voilà!

SOFTLY SCRAMBLED *eggs*

Beaten eggs cooked over gentle heat with just the right amount of stirring are one of the world's most glorious foods. Here you will find a few ways to softly scramble eggs, each yielding a distinctly different texture. What they all have in common is that the outcome is moist, soft, and supple eggs.

Scrambled eggs made quickly and haphazardly in a hot pan are most often rubbery, dry, unremarkable things. I find this to be true of most large-curd scrambled eggs served at breakfast joints across America. A splash of milk, cream, or water beaten in to the eggs helps to keep them moist, as does pulling the pan from the heat at just the right moment, when the eggs are still glistening.

French-style scrambled eggs are traditionally made in a double boiler. They are stirred constantly, for as long as 20 minutes, until the gentle heat transforms them to a saucy, custard-like consistency. My method results in the same creamy eggs, similar to the consistency of polenta, in a matter of minutes—it just takes a little arm workout with a whisk.

Scrambled eggs are delicious on their own with just a hint of salt and pepper. Or get creative with the addition of cheese, herbs, and other aromatic seasonings, or cooked vegetables, meats, or seafood. How about adding in steamed mussels for a clever play? Throw in a pinch of saffron or turmeric for a brilliantly hued scramble. Try duck eggs for an extra-rich rendition. Stir in pesto and garnish with ribbons of thinly sliced prosciutto for a tasty take on green eggs and ham.

KEYS TO SOFTLY SCRAMBLING EGGS:

• Cook them over gentle heat. If you have a gas stove and know the heat doesn't get very low, use a heat diffuser, or pull the pan from the heat occasionally as the eggs cook.

• Scramble two or three large eggs per person, depending on how they will be served and how hungry you are.

• Fats and liquids, such as butter, cream, or oil, added to the eggs will produce softer curds. But if the eggs are overcooked, the liquid will separate from the eggs in a watery mess.

• Residual heat will continue to cook the eggs, so always remove them from the pan when they are moist and just a little underdone.

• Vegetables, meat, and seafood should be precooked before mixing in. The short time that the eggs take to scramble surely won't be long enough to cook things like bacon or mushrooms, plus those ingredients release water as they cook, which will dilute the eggs. Mix-ins should be added at room temperature (cheese and herbs) or warm (vegetables and meat), rather than piping hot or cold.

• Choosing the right pan is important. It should be a nonstick sauté pan, or a well-seasoned cast-iron skillet, if you prefer. Size matters: To keep the eggs from cooking too quickly, it must be small enough to contain them in at least a ½-in/12-mm layer, but large enough to be able to stir them comfortably without bits of egg spilling over the sides.

Number of Large Eggs to Scramble	Ideal Pan Size
2 or 3	4½ to 6 in/11 to 15 cm
4 or 5	8 in/20 cm
6 to 8	10 in/25 cm
More than 8	12 in/30.5 cm

scrambled eggs, two ways

serves 1 (multiply for more servings)

Whether you prefer large, fluffy curds or small, creamy ones, the key to delicate scrambled eggs is to get them out of the pan while they're still a little moist and glistening.

THE AMERICAN WAY: SOFT, FLUFFY CURDS

INGREDIENTS

½ tbsp unsalted butter

2 farm-fresh eggs

½ tbsp milk, heavy (whipping) cream, or water

¼ tsp fine sea salt

Pinch of freshly ground pepper (optional)

Mix-ins of your choice, such as chopped fresh herbs, cooked meat or vegetables, or finely grated or crumbled cheese

PREPARATION

Melt the butter in a nonstick sauté pan (for pan size, see chart on page 47) over medium heat. Whisk the eggs in a large bowl with the milk, salt, and pepper, if using, until foamy, but avoid aggressively beating.

When the butter melts and little bubbles appear, reduce the heat to low on a gas stove or medium-low on an electric stove, and pour the eggs into the pan. Let a thin layer of egg set on the bottom, about 30 seconds, then scrape the pan with a flat-bottomed wooden spoon or a heat-resistant spatula. Redistribute the liquid eggs to coat the bottom of the pan and wait another 20 seconds or so for another layer of egg to set. Scrape that layer from the bottom and redistribute the uncooked egg. Continue this process until the eggs are all cooked into large, creamy curds that are still quite moist and shiny, reducing the heat or pulling the pan away from the burner for a few seconds if they begin to cook too quickly. The process should take 3 to 4 minutes.

Stir in any mix-ins with about 1 minute left to cook. When the eggs are still just a little creamy and loose, slide them out of the pan and onto a warmed plate to serve.

continued

SOFTLY SCRAMBLED EGGS

THE FRENCH WAY: CREAMY, SAUCY CUSTARD

INGREDIENTS

½ tbsp unsalted butter

2 farm-fresh eggs

¼ tsp fine sea salt

Pinch of freshly ground pepper (optional)

Mix-ins of your choice, such as chopped fresh herbs, cooked meat or vegetables, or finely grated or crumbled cheese

1 tbsp milk or heavy (whipping) cream

PREPARATION

Melt the butter in a nonstick sauté pan (for pan size, see chart on page 47) over medium heat. Whisk the eggs in a large bowl with the salt and pepper, if using, until foamy, but avoid aggressively beating.

When the butter is melted and little bubbles appear, reduce the heat to low on a gas stove or medium-low on an electric stove, and pour the eggs into the pan. Immediately begin whisking the eggs, vigorously and constantly, using the side of the whisk to cover more surface area and applying gentle pressure to avoid chipping the bottom of the pan. When the eggs begin to thicken, after about 1 minute, stir in any mix-ins. When the eggs are uniformly thickened and saucy, add the milk and remove the pan from the heat to arrest the cooking. Continue whisking as the residual heat from the pan finishes the eggs to a custard-like consistency. The total cooking time is only about 2 minutes.

Spoon the eggs from the pan onto the dish they are destined for, such as a piece of buttery toasted baguette. (Jean-Georges Vongerichten spoons them back into the eggshell and garnishes them with whipped cream and caviar. Michel Roux serves them in hollowed roasted baby potatoes.) Serve immediately.

POACHED SCRAMBLED EGGS

serves 2

This technique is the brainchild of San Francisco chef Daniel Patterson. He came up with the idea to appease his then-fiancée, an environmental lawyer who made him throw out his Teflon-coated egg pan. Incredibly light and fluffy, this is a pure and simple expression of the egg. Crème fraîche and caviar, sour cream and chives, olive oil and a pinch of piment d'Espelette, these are all delicious toppings that add richness and depth.

INGREDIENTS

Salt

4 farm-fresh eggs, cold

PREPARATION

Fill a medium saucepan with about 4 in/10 cm of water, season with salt, and bring to a simmer over medium-high heat. Set a colander in the sink.

If the eggs are not extremely fresh, strain away the thin whites: One at a time, crack the eggs into a slotted spoon or large-mesh strainer set over a bowl to strain away the thin white (don't use a fine-mesh strainer, or the thin whites won't be able to filter through).

Put the eggs into a large mixing bowl and beat vigorously until foamy and homogenous, about 20 seconds.

Using a large spoon, vigorously swirl the simmering water until a whirlpool forms in the center. Lower the bowl of eggs down to the center of the swirling water so that the lip of the bowl touches the water, and let the eggs slip into the vortex. Immediately cover the pot and cook the eggs for 20 to 30 seconds.

Remove the saucepan from the heat. The eggs should be floating on the surface of the water in a shaggy mass. Pour the water from the saucepan over the colander set in the sink while holding back the eggs with a slotted spoon or large-mesh skimmer. The colander will catch any loose bits of egg. Carefully slide the eggs into the colander, and press them gently with the spoon while tilting the strainer to extract as much water as possible. Let them drain for 30 seconds to 1 minute. Gently slide the eggs onto a plate, or divide them between two, and season with salt before serving.

caramelized onion matzo brei

serves 4

Though it's more traditional to scramble eggs mixed with soggy matzo in schmaltz, caramelized onions and brown butter elevate this classic Jewish breakfast to a new level of sophistication. This recipe is an updated version of one that I created as a consultant on a book about modern Jewish deli cuisine, The Artisan Jewish Deli at Home, *by Nick Zukin and Michael Zusman.*

INGREDIENTS

3 tbsp unsalted butter

½ large yellow onion, thinly sliced

Salt and freshly ground pepper

4 matzo boards, broken into 1½-in/4-cm pieces

1 cup/240 ml milk, warm

10 room-temperature farm-fresh eggs

2 tbsp chopped fresh parsley

Sour cream for garnish

Applesauce for serving

PREPARATION

Melt the butter in a large nonstick sauté pan over medium heat. When it's bubbly, add the onion and a pinch of salt and pepper and cook, stirring occasionally, until the onion is evenly browned and the butter takes on a golden-brown hue, 12 to 15 minutes.

Meanwhile, in a medium bowl, soak the matzo in the warm milk until soft but still a little crisp inside, about 2 minutes. Drain in a colander and gently press to squeeze out excess moisture. Whisk the eggs in a large bowl with a pinch of salt and pepper. Stir the matzo into the egg mixture just before cooking.

Reduce the heat to low on a gas stove or medium-low on an electric stove, and pour the egg mixture into the pan, spreading it out in an even layer with the onions. Let a thin layer of egg set on the bottom, about 30 seconds, then scrape the pan with a flat-bottomed wooden spoon or a heat-resistant spatula. Redistribute the liquid eggs to coat the bottom of the pan and wait another 20 seconds or so for another layer of egg to set. Scrape that layer from the bottom and redistribute the uncooked egg. Continue this process until the eggs are all cooked into large, creamy curds that are still quite moist and shiny, reducing the heat or pulling the pan away from the burner for a few seconds if they begin to cook too quickly. The process should take 3 to 4 minutes.

Stir in the parsley with about 1 minute left to cook. When the eggs are still just a little creamy and loose, slide the matzo brei out of the pan and onto warmed plates. Top with a dollop of sour cream and serve with ramekins of applesauce.

FRIED EGGS

Nicely panfried eggs require little more than the right amount of heat, a smidgen of flavorful fat, and the correct pan for the job. The goal is to set the whites in a tender state while cooking the yolks to your preferred degree of doneness. For me, that is sunny-side up or over easy. In *The Wine and Food Society's Guide to Eggs* (1968), author Margaret Sherman wrote, "Some prefer to turn the eggs over with a fish slice (spatula) as soon as it starts to set, though gastronomically it seems to me to be somehow brutal, except when the extra sealing is necessary for fried egg sandwiches." I agree that there are a few delectable uses for eggs flipped and cooked to the point that the yolks thicken to a molten consistency.

Deep-fat frying is an underutilized method with eggs. Egg whites have the ability to brown when exposed to high heat, creating a crisp,

brittle shell. When first rolled in bread crumbs, the contrasting textures of a light and crispy coating to cloak a silky, oozing yolk may be your new favorite way to eat an egg. It sure is mine.

With a food as simple and pure in flavor as an egg, the fat in which you fry it plays a big role. For cooking eggs over moderate heat, go for fats that will season the eggs, such as olive oil, butter, duck or chicken fat, lard, clarified butter, ghee, or bacon drippings. Oil with a relatively high smoke point is necessary when cooking over exceptionally high heat, such as with Wok-Fried Eggs (page 64), when crispiness is the goal and caramelization the flavor gain.

A good, heavy nonstick skillet is crucial for panfrying. There's nothing that can do the job of Teflon, in terms of ease in sliding eggs around to flip or slide onto a plate. If you're worried about using Teflon over higher heats, try one of the newer eco-friendly nonstick ceramic pans. A French chef I used to work for favored a well-seasoned black steel pan, which is wonderful for a multitude of other things, e.g., crêpes. Many American cooks swear by their seasoned cast-iron pans, and I love the romantic notion of a shiny, dark patina from years, perhaps generations, of use. If you choose to use one of the latter two, just be sure to use a little extra fat and that it's sizzling hot before the eggs are added to prevent sticking.

Keys to nicely panfried eggs:

• *The fresher the eggs, the better. As eggs age, the plump white surrounding the yolk breaks down into a stringy thin white, causing too much spread in the pan.*

• *For classic fried eggs, use just enough fat to lightly coat the pan in beady droplets, not so much as a puddle. Other techniques in this section call for more fat to achieve crispy results.*

• *With sunny-side up eggs, wait to season the eggs with salt until after they are cooked, to avoid welted, spotty marks on the yolks.*

• *The tasks at hand are to ensure that the tops of the eggs cook at the same time as the bottoms do and to cook the yolks to your desired degree of doneness. The following recipes explore a few ways of achieving that goal.*

• *With a little practice and a slope-sided nonstick sauté pan, one or two eggs can be tossed in the air to flip with a quick sweeping motion of the arm.*

• *The size of the pan is important. Choose one that is just wide enough for the number of eggs you're going to cook, meaning that the thick whites can spread freely, but the thin whites are contained, to avoid stringy, jagged edges.*

Number of Large Eggs to Fry	Ideal Pan Size
1	4.5 to 6 in/11 to 15 cm
2	8 in/20 cm
3 or 4	10 in/25 cm
5 or 6	12 in/30.5 cm
More than 6	Fry in batches!

PANFRIED EGGS WITH VARYING DEGREES OF DONENESS

BASIC PREPARATION

Heat a nonstick skillet over low to medium-low heat and add just enough fat to lightly coat, about ½ tsp per egg. Butter is hot enough when it begins to lightly bubble; rendered fats and oils are hot enough when a drop of water added to the pan gently sizzles. Slip the eggs into the pan, evenly spaced if cooking more than one. When the eggs are done to your liking (see following preparations), slide them out of the pan with the aid of a spatula and onto a warmed plate or directly onto the dish they are destined for. Season them with salt and pepper before serving.

SUNNY-SIDE UP

PREPARATION

Skipping the flipping required to prepare over-easy eggs ensures unbroken yolks, but getting the tops done at the same time as the undersides can be a challenge. Since they're not turned, the eggs should be cooked over low heat and covered after about 1 minute, once the thin whites set, to reflect heat onto the tops. Even still, the film of white covering the yolk remains uncooked, which is OK if you ask me because the yolks stay perky and radiant. To set that film of white, add a splash of water to the pan before covering to steam the tops opaque. (A clever name I've heard for this method is "looking-glass eggs.") The total cooking time is about 4 minutes.

SUNNY-SIDE UP FROM THE OVEN

PREPARATION

The French refer to this technique as *oeufs sur le plat* (eggs on the plate). Cook the eggs just as for sunny-side up, until the bottom whites are just set, about 1 minute. Transfer the pan to a hot oven (350°F/180°F/gas 4 or higher) to finish cooking the tops, about 2 minutes for runny, bright yellow yolks, or 3 to 4 minutes for the thin sheath of white covering the yolks to turn opaque. Be sure that the pan is ovenproof.

sunny-side up

sunny-side up from the oven

FRIED QUAIL EGGS

PREPARATION

Cook up to five quail eggs at a time in an 8-in/20-cm skillet so that they have room to fully spread and you have room to maneuver a spatula. Using the sunny-side up method, cook them for 1½ to 2 minutes; they look best when the yolks are left bright yellow rather than steamed opaque, so I highly recommend that you forgo adding a splash of water to the pan. The shells are a little difficult to crack: Use the tip of a knife to gently slice an opening in the wide end of each shell, just large enough for the egg to slip out. Stand them up in the carton they came in until the pan is hot. One at a time, pour them from their shells into the hot pan, working quickly so they will be done at about the same time.

continued

over easy

PREPARATION

Some refer to these as "dippy eggs" because that's what you do with a piece of toast in their runny yolks. Cook the eggs over medium-low heat. When the bottom of the whites are set, after about 1 minute, carefully turn the eggs with a spatula or gently toss them from the pan to flip. Briefly finish off the tops while leaving the yolk runny, which takes about 20 seconds.

over medium

PREPARATION

Eggs have creamy, thickened yolks with barely molten centers when they are done exactly as for over easy but on low heat for 1½ to 2 minutes per side. These are great on breakfast sandwiches, because the yolk is soft and rich but won't make a mess when you take a bite.

over hard

PREPARATION

Start with room-temperature eggs. It's tricky to fully cook the yolks without turning the whites into rubbery, leathery, pitiful things. The only way that fair-textured whites can be achieved in unison with set yolks is by breaking the yolks by poking them with a fork just before flipping so that they cook more quickly. Cook over low heat until the whites are set, 2½ to 3 minutes, then poke the yokes with a fork to break, flip, and continue cooking until the yolks are fully set, about 2½ to 3 minutes more.

over easy

over medium

over hard

gone!

eGGS FLaVORFULLY BaSTeD

makes 2 eggs

Basting eggs is a variation of the sunny-side up technique. It works best when cooking just two eggs at a time. The point is to gently cook and season the tops of the eggs by spooning them with hot, flavorful fat. Try duck fat, bacon drippings, schmaltz, or fruity olive oil. To make a pan sauce, you can sauté a teaspoon or so of minced shallots in the fat remaining in the pan. Finish with a splash of vinegar and a sprinkle of herbs and spoon it over the eggs.

INGREDIENTS

¼ cup/60 ml fat, such as duck fat, bacon drippings, schmaltz, or fruity olive oil

2 room-temperature eggs

PREPARATION

Heat the fat in a nonstick skillet over medium-low heat. When it's shimmering hot, add the eggs. When the bottoms just turn opaque, tilt the pan to collect a pool of fat and begin spooning the fat over the tops of the eggs. It will take about 2 minutes for set whites and runny yolks. Slide the eggs out of the pan, holding back the excess fat, and onto a plate or directly onto the dish they are destined for.

CRISPY FRIED EGGS

makes 2 eggs

This technique builds flavor and varied texture in panfried eggs. The eggs are cooked in a super-hot pan, so that the whites get just a little crispy but the yolks remain runny within. Waiting until the fat is almost at the smoking point is key. The eggs bubble and spurt and crisp up quickly at the edges. A drizzle of lemon juice or vinegar is added to create steam, and the pan is covered with a tight-fitting lid to trap it in, finishing off the tops of the eggs. Aromatic ingredients, like garlic, red pepper flakes, and herbs, add tremendous flavor to eggs cooked in this manner; get creative with your own twists on the following variations. Be aware that the cooking happens fast, and these ingredients burn easily, so it's important to have each one ready to go into the pan. Have the eggs cracked into little dishes and any aromatics sliced, juiced, and measured out next to the stove top.

PREPARATION

Heat a nonstick skillet over medium-high heat, then add the oil. When it's shimmering hot, crack in the eggs (watch for splatter!). The bottoms of the whites will set almost on contact. When they do, sprinkle with the salt and lemon juice, and immediately cover the pan with a lid. Let the eggs finish cooking, 30 to 45 seconds for runny yolks or 1 to 1½ minutes for molten yolks. Slide them out of the pan and onto a plate or directly onto the dish they are destined for. Sprinkle with pepper.

continued

INGREDIENTS

1 tbsp olive oil

2 room-temperature eggs

Pinch of salt

1½ tsp fresh lemon juice or fruity vinegar, such as balsamic, sherry, or cider

Freshly ground pepper

GaRLic-cHiLe eGGS

makes 2 eggs

INGREDIENTS

2 tbsp olive oil

4 large garlic cloves, thinly sliced

¼ to ½ tsp red pepper flakes, or to taste

2 room-temperature eggs

Pinch of salt

½ tsp fresh lemon juice or water

PREPARATION

Heat a nonstick skillet over medium-high heat, then add the oil. When it's shimmering hot, add the garlic and pepper flakes, stir very briefly to coat them with fat, then quickly crack in the eggs (watch for splatter!). The bottoms of the whites will set almost on contact. When they do, sprinkle with the salt and lemon juice, and immediately cover the pan with a lid. Let the eggs finish cooking, 30 to 45 seconds for runny yolks or 1 to 1½ minutes for molten yolks. Slide them out of the pan and onto a plate or directly onto the dish they are destined for.

SaGe–BROWn BUTTeR eGGS

makes 2 eggs

INGREDIENTS

2 tbsp unsalted butter

4 to 6 fresh sage leaves

Salt

2 room-temperature eggs

½ tsp fresh lemon juice

PREPARATION

Melt the butter in a nonstick skillet over medium heat. When it's bubbly, add the sage leaves and fry until crisp, using tongs to turn them once, about 2 minutes; you'll know they're crisp when they stop sizzling. Transfer the fried leaves to a plate lined with a paper towel and sprinkle them with salt. At this point the butter will be starting to brown. Quickly crack the eggs into the pan (watch for splatter!). The bottom of the whites will set almost on contact. When they do, sprinkle with a pinch of salt and the lemon juice, and immediately cover the pan with a lid. Let the eggs finish cooking, about 45 seconds to 1 minute for runny yolks, or 1½ to 2 minutes for molten yolks. Slide them out of the pan and onto a plate or directly onto the dish they are destined for. Drizzle with the brown butter left in the pan and garnish with the fried sage.

WOK-FRIED EGGS

makes 2 egg-

When eggs are fried over high heat in a well-seasoned wok, the edges turn crunchy, and the tops and bottoms crisp and turn a deep golden brown. The best part is that the yolks stay fluid and saucy, to moisten fried rice, stir-fried noodles, or vegetables. To get the best results, be sure that the oil is smoking hot before adding the eggs, and don't fry more than two at a time. If you're looking to feed four, simply repeat.

INGREDIENTS

3 tbsp peanut or vegetable oil

2 room-temperature eggs

Pinch of salt

PREPARATION

Heat a seasoned carbon-steel or nonstick flat-bottomed wok over high heat. Add the oil and swirl to coat the bottom and edges of the pan. When you begin to see wisps of smoke, add the eggs; they will spit and splatter enthusiastically. After about 45 seconds, the eggs will be crispy and browned on the bottom. Turn the eggs, flipping away from you to avoid splatter, and cook until crisp and browned on the other side, 30 to 45 seconds more. Transfer the eggs to a plate lined with a paper towel, or directly onto the dish they are destined for. Sprinkle with the salt right away.

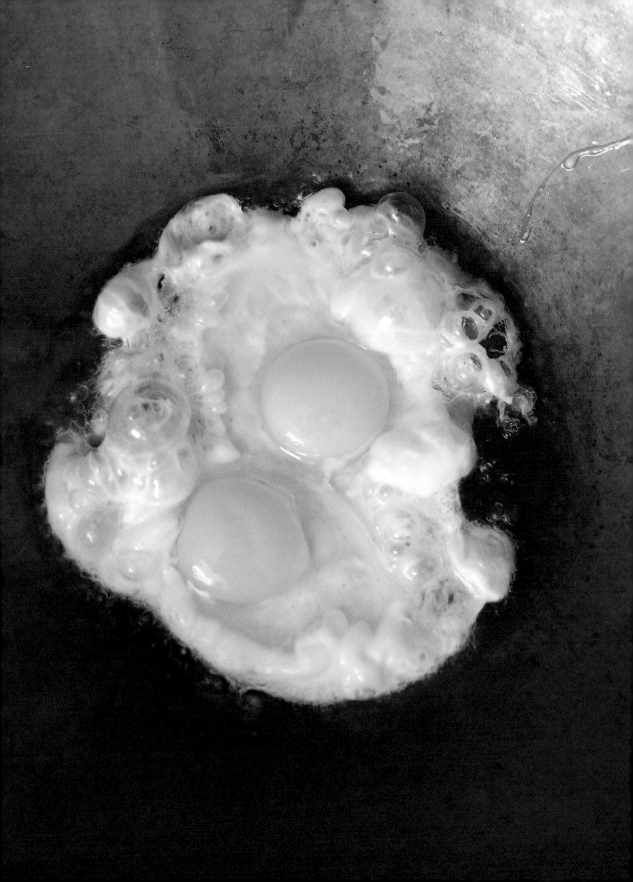

CRUNCHY DEEP-FRIED EGGS

makes 2 eggs

Deep-frying eggs is a cinch once you get down the routine. The eggs don't absorb as much oil as you may think, and the presentation is positively impressive, with crispy whites enclosing a molten yolk. Try switching up the fat for added flavor to complement the dish they will be served on. Duck fat, lard, and clarified butter are all good options.

INGREDIENTS

Peanut or vegetable oil for deep-frying

2 room-temperature eggs

Pinch of salt

PREPARATION

Fill a small, heavy saucepan with about 1½ in/ 4 cm of oil and heat it over medium-high heat until a deep-frying thermometer registers 350°F/180°C. Adjust the heat to maintain the temperature.

Crack the eggs into small dishes first, and then lower the dish down to the surface of the oil and gently slip the eggs in (watch for splatter!). Wait 5 to 10 seconds for the egg whites to just begin to set, then use two heat-proof spoons to carefully fold up the edges of the whites over the yolks to encase them. Fry until the whites are set and lightly browned and crispy at the edges, about 1 minute. Remove the eggs with a slotted spoon, place them on a plate lined with a paper towel, and sprinkle with the salt. Repeat to fry more eggs, if you'd like. Serve right away.

BREADED EGGS

makes 4 eggs

Breading a soft-cooked egg before deep-frying yields a crispy crust to crack into, and a creamy, barely flowing yolk within. These make a lovely appetizer all on their own, sliced in half and seasoned with a pinch of nice salt. Or serve them on a salad, like Frisée aux Lardons and Crispy Breaded Eggs (page 148), and nix the croutons.

INGREDIENTS

Peanut or vegetable oil for deep-frying

¼ cup/30 g all-purpose flour

1 egg white, lightly beaten

½ cup/85 g fine dried bread crumbs

2 tbsp very finely chopped fresh parsley or other herbs

Salt

Four 5-Minute Eggs (see page 28)

PREPARATION

Fill a 3- to 4-qt/2.8- to 3.8-L heavy saucepan with about 1½ in/4 cm of oil and heat it over medium-high heat until a deep-frying thermometer registers 375°F/190°C. Adjust the heat to maintain the temperature.

Set up a three-step breading assembly line with one shallow dish containing the flour, a second shallow dish with the egg white, and a third shallow dish with the bread crumbs, parsley, and a big pinch of salt mixed together. One at a time, gently roll the eggs in the flour to coat with a thin film. Then dip in the egg white and shake off the excess. Finally, roll in the bread crumb mixture to gather an even coating. Collect the breaded eggs on a plate.

One at a time, lower the eggs into the oil using a slotted spoon. (You can fry them all at once if your pan is wide enough, or two at a time.) Fry until crisp and golden brown, 15 to 30 seconds. Transfer the fried eggs to a plate lined with a paper towel to drain, sprinkle with salt, and serve right away. They can be cut in half or served whole, depending on the application.

BAKED AND BROILED EGGS

Eggs can be baked or broiled atop casseroles and gratins, sauces and stews, or in edible shells of ham, bready things like phyllo, or hollowed vegetables like squash or mushroom caps.

As with all egg cookery, timing is of the essence: to catch the egg when it is at the perfect state of solid yet tender, set on the outside while loose inside. This takes a properly sized dish and consideration of the heat source. If it comes from above, you're broiling; from all around, you're baking. My typical rule of thumb is to broil the eggs if they are placed atop anything that is saucy and piping hot, such as tomato sauce or Basque Pipérade Beans (see page 184). The hot liquid will gently cook the eggs from below, while the broiler gets them from above. Placed over cold or dry foods, like in Eggs Baked on Crisped Bread and Kale Salad (page 73), they should be baked; the hot oven must envelop the eggs to heat both the bottoms and the tops in equal measure.

In the following recipes, the eggs can be baked or broiled individually, in pairs, or with several in one dish. Just be sure to choose a shallow baking dish that contains them snuggled in a single layer.

Number of Eggs	Volume or Size of Baking Dish
1	¾ cup/180 ml; 5 by 5 by 1 in/12 by 12 by 2.5 cm
2	1½ cups/360 ml; 6 by 6 by 1½ in/15 by 15 by 4 cm
3 or 4	1 qt/960 ml; 7 by 10 by 1½ in/17 by 25 by 4 cm
5 or 6	1½ qt/1.4 L ; 8 by 12 by 2 in/20 by 30.5 by 5 cm

Keys to properly baking and broiling eggs:

· For baking, eggs should be placed in the center of the oven, and 325°F/165°C/gas 3 seems to be the magic temperature to achieve set whites at the precise time that the yolks are thickened but still molten. You'll see that the whites are visibly set and the yolks jiggle when the dish is gently shaken. This will take 10 to 15 minutes, but rely more on the look of the eggs than on the timing. If you prefer yolks a bit firmer, or if you're using duck eggs, bake them a little longer, say 15 to 20 minutes.

· To broil eggs, position the oven rack in the top slot, or about 4 in/10 cm from the broiler heating element. They take about 5 minutes for set whites and loose yolks, for either chicken or duck eggs. To cook the yolks past molten, position the rack in the center of the oven so as not to burn the tops before the eggs cook through, which will take 8 to 10 minutes for medium yolks, and 10 to 12 minutes for fully cooked.

oven eggs with olive oil and dukkah

serves 1 (multiply for more servings)

Here the eggs are cooked in a bath of olive oil for an extra-delicate texture. Dukkah, an Egyptian spice and nut blend, is meant for dipping, and that's just what you'll do with this dish: Dip in chunks of bread or pita to swoop up the seasoned eggs and oil.

INGREDIENTS

2 tbsp extra-virgin olive oil

2 room-temperature eggs

1 tbsp Dukkah (recipe follows)

Toasted bread or pita for serving

PREPARATION

Preheat the oven to 325°F/165°C/gas 3. Pour the oil into the bottom of a shallow baking dish that's just big enough to contain the number of eggs you are baking (see chart on page 55). Crack in the eggs and sprinkle Dukkah over the top. Bake to your desired doneness, 10 to 15 minutes for loose yolks, 15 to 20 minutes for partially or fully set yolks. Serve with thick slices of country bread or pita wedges, toasted if desired.

DUKKAH

makes a scant ½ cup/50 g

INGREDIENTS

1 tbsp coriander seeds

½ tsp peppercorns

1 tbsp fennel seeds

½ tbsp cumin seeds

3 tbsp roasted unsalted pistachios or hazelnuts

1 tbsp sesame seeds

¼ tsp salt

PREPARATION

Heat a small sauté pan or skillet over medium heat. When it's hot, add the coriander and peppercorns and toast, constantly swirling the pan over the heat until aromatic, about 30 seconds. Add the fennel and continue swirling and toasting about 30 seconds more. Add the cumin and continue toasting until pungent. When completely cool, grind the spices in a spice grinder or mortar and pestle to tiny pieces, but not a powder. Add the pistachios and grind or pound them to small crumbs, taking care not to overwork the mixture into a paste. The texture should be like homemade bread crumbs. Stir in the sesame seeds and salt. The dukkah will keep in an airtight container in the refrigerator for a few weeks.

eGGS BaKeD WITH MUSHROOMS, THYMe, anD CReaM

serves 4 as an appetizer, 2 as a main

The classic combination of eggs, mushrooms, and cream is enhanced only by the addition of shaved fresh truffles, if you are lucky enough to (1) find them and (2) afford them. If you do have fresh truffles, put them and the eggs, still in their shells, in a glass container. Cover it and refrigerate for a day or two, to allow the flavor to permeate the eggs. After baking, shave the truffles over the top of the dish. Or, if you have truffle salt or butter, use either in place of plain salt or butter in this recipe.

INGREDIENTS

6 oz/170 g meaty mushrooms, such as porcini, chanterelles, matsutakes, or cremini

2 tbsp unsalted butter

2 tsp fresh thyme leaves

Salt

4 room-temperature eggs

¼ cup/60 ml heavy (whipping) cream

Freshly ground pepper

PREPARATION

Preheat the oven to 325°F/165°C/gas 3. Clean the mushrooms and cut or tear them into bite-size pieces. Heat a 10-in/25-cm sauté pan or skillet over medium-high heat. Add the butter and swirl to melt and coat the pan. When the foam subsides, add the mushrooms. Sauté until they give up their liquid and it evaporates, about 3 minutes, then add the thyme and a pinch of salt. Continue sautéing until the mushrooms are lightly browned, about 2 minutes more. Scrape the contents of the pan into a shallow baking dish, or divide it between two, being sure to get all the butter and herbs. Create spaces in the mushrooms for the eggs and crack them in. Pour the cream around the egg whites. Bake to your desired doneness, 10 to 15 minutes for loose yolks and 15 to 20 minutes for partially or fully set yolks. Season the eggs with salt and pepper and serve.

eggs baked on crisped bread and kale salad

serves 4 as an appetizer, 2 as a main

Here's an interesting change from your regular brunch routine. This twist on Italian bread salad makes a texturally intriguing base for baked eggs. The dish is especially lovely when the yolks are served runny, as a rich sauce to be soaked up by the crisped bread.

INGREDIENTS

8 oz/225 g day-old whole-grain artisan bread (about ½ loaf), crusts removed, torn into large bite-size chunks

3 tbsp extra-virgin olive oil

3 cups/60 g lightly packed kale leaves torn into bite-size pieces

2 tbsp roasted unsalted pistachios

1 large shallot, thinly sliced

2 garlic cloves, thinly sliced

¼ cup/60 ml homemade chicken or vegetable stock or store-bought low-sodium broth

¼ cup/40 g halved dried Italian plums (or prunes)

1½ tbsp white wine vinegar, or to taste

Salt

Freshly ground pepper

4 room-temperature eggs

PREPARATION

Position an oven rack about 4 in/10 cm from the top heating element and preheat the broiler.

Toss the bread in a large bowl with 1 tbsp of the oil to very lightly coat. Spread the bread out on a rimmed baking sheet and broil until the edges are lightly toasted and crisp, turning once, about 3 minutes. Return the toasted bread to the bowl and add the kale and pistachios, leaving the kale mounded on top.

Switch the oven to bake at 325°F/165°C/gas 3.

Heat the remaining 2 tbsp oil in a small sauté pan over medium-low heat. When it's shimmering hot, add the shallot and garlic and cook until soft but not brown, 3 to 5 minutes. Stir in the stock, plums, vinegar, ½ tsp salt, and a pinch of pepper to make a dressing, and warm to just below a simmer, about 1 minute.

Drizzle the warm dressing over the salad and toss together to thoroughly coat, saturating the bread and wilting the kale. Taste a piece of the bread and add more salt, pepper, or vinegar as needed.

Put the salad in a shallow baking dish, or divide it between two. Crack the eggs over the top, spacing them evenly. Bake to your desired doneness, 10 to 15 minutes for loose yolks and 15 to 20 minutes for partially or fully set yolks. Season the eggs with salt and pepper and serve.

eGGS In PURGaTORY

serves 4 as an appetizer, 2 as a main

Religious metaphor aside, eggs cooked in tomato sauce is a classic combination. This sauce is a riff on Marcella Hazan's classic, simple, and delicious sauce of tomatoes stewed with onions and butter. Here it's spiced up with a pinch of red pepper flakes. When the eggs are cracked over the hot sauce, the cooking process begins. The broiler finishes them off from above, under a blanket of crusty cheese. A hunk of bread is essential for dipping at breakfast, but for lunch or dinner, I prefer a coil of buttered noodles alongside.

INGREDIENTS

Spicy Tomato Sauce with Onion and Butter

One 14½-oz/415-g can diced tomatoes

½ onion, halved again through the root

3 tbsp unsalted butter

1 tsp salt

Pinch of red pepper flakes

4 room-temperature eggs

¼ cup/30 g freshly grated Pecorino Romano or Parmigiano-Reggiano cheese

Bread or noodles for serving

PREPARATION

To make the sauce: Put the tomatoes, onion, butter, salt, and pepper flakes in a small saucepan and bring to a simmer over medium-high heat. Reduce the heat to maintain a low simmer and cook, stirring occasionally, until the tomatoes are infused with the onion flavor and the butter appears in glossy swells on the surface, about 45 minutes. If needed, add more salt or pepper flakes. (Marcella discards the onion, but sometimes I coarsely chop it and add it back in to the sauce.)

Position an oven rack about 4 in/10 cm from the top heating element for loose yolks or in the center of the oven for partially or fully set yolks. Preheat the broiler. Spread the hot tomato sauce to cover the bottom of a shallow baking dish that will just fit the eggs in a single layer, or divide it between two. Crack in the eggs and sprinkle them with the cheese. Broil until the cheese is melted and crusty, the egg whites are set, and the yolks are cooked to your desired doneness, 5 minutes for loose and 8 to 10 minutes for firm. Cool for a few minutes, then serve the eggs and sauce over bread or noodles.

PRESERVED EGGS

There was a time when eggs had their season, just like spring peas or juicy, ripe tomatoes. Hens laid eggs in a natural cycle, beginning in the spring and ending in the fall. To get through the winter months, our ancestors employed resourceful ways of preserving them. Here are a few of them.

SALTED EGGS

Salted eggs are a mainstay of Chinese cuisine, dating back to a time when eggs were in season from spring through fall. Brined eggs made it through the winter. To make them, eggs are submerged in salty water for about a month, which inhibits the growth of bacteria and transforms the yolks to firm, bright orangish-red orbs. Oddly, the whites remain translucent but become completely liquefied. After brining, they are hard-cooked and eaten as a snack or as an accoutrement to congee or salads, and the yolks play a starring role in Chinese moon cakes.

PICKLED EGGS

Pickling is an age-old means of preservation, but with the advent of refrigeration, we now pickle eggs purely for pleasure. The following recipes could be considered quick-pickled eggs, with the goal of dyeing the whites with a brilliant hue and imparting robust flavor, while keeping them tender. These aren't fully pickled to put up, which turns the whites quite rubbery. Gently pickled eggs with brightly colored whites make rather impressive deviled eggs or colorful accoutrements on a charcuterie board. The procedure for pickling quail or duck eggs is exactly the same, though you may be able to fit only seven duck eggs in the brine, and many more quail eggs—at least a dozen—which will pickle a little more quickly, too.

salted eggs

Typically duck eggs are salted for preservation, but the technique works for chicken eggs, too. Eat the boiled salted eggs all by their lonesome, or grate them over a salad, such as Spicy and Herbaceous Thai Salad with Salted Duck Eggs (page 142).

INGREDIENTS

⅔ cup/165 g sea salt

1 star anise pod (optional)

1 tbsp Shaoxing wine (optional; see Cook's Note)

8 duck eggs or 10 chicken eggs

PREPARATION

Put the salt in a small saucepan and pour in 2 cups/480 ml water. Add the star anise and wine, if using. Bring the mixture to a boil over high heat, stirring until the salt is dissolved. Remove the pan from the heat and let the brine cool to room temperature.

Meanwhile, scrub the eggshells under cold water. Carefully place the eggs in a clean 1-qt/960-ml jar or other lidded container. Be sure that the eggs are free of even hairline cracks that could ruin the whole batch.

Pour the cooled brine over the eggs and push them down to submerge. Some may bob to the surface, so place a small dish over the top to weight them down. Tightly cover the jar and leave it in a dark place at room temperature for the brine to penetrate the eggs all the way through the yolk. This may take from 20 to 30 days for chicken eggs, and up to 40 days for duck eggs.

Begin checking the eggs after 3 weeks have passed. Crack an egg into a dish. The egg white should be transparent and fluid, but you're really looking to see if the yolk has firmed and transformed to orangish-red all the way through. If it's not quite there, wait a few more days, then check another egg. When they are sufficiently preserved, drain, dry, and store the eggs in an egg carton in the refrigerator. They keep for at least 6 weeks, uncooked.

Cook the salted eggs as you would for Simmered Eggs (page 27), 15 minutes for chicken eggs and 20 minutes for duck eggs.

cook's note: *Shaoxing wine is a Chinese fermented rice wine. It is easy to find at Asian markets and in many grocery stores.*

BeeT-PICKLeD eGGS

makes 8 eggs

I like to devil these stunning, magenta-colored eggs for a radiant twist, or slice them over salads, like the vibrant Picnic Salad of Wheat Berries, Favas, Radishes, and Beet Pickled Eggs on page 143.

INGREDIENTS

½ cup/120 ml red wine vinegar

1 medium red beet, trimmed, peeled, and thinly sliced

½ cup/100 g sugar

1 tbsp sea or kosher salt

1 tsp pink peppercorns or ½ tsp black peppercorns

1 bay leaf

1 clove

Eight 13-Minute Eggs (see page 28), peeled

PREPARATION

Bring the vinegar, beet slices, sugar, salt, peppercorns, bay leaf, clove, and 2 cups/ 480 ml water to a boil in a small saucepan over medium-high heat, stirring until the salt and sugar are dissolved. Reduce the heat to maintain a low simmer, cover, and cook until the beet slices are tender, about 15 minutes. Remove from the heat and cool to room temperature.

Put the eggs in a container that will hold them and the pickling brine comfortably. Pour the cooled brine, beet slices and all, over the eggs and push them down to submerge. Cover and refrigerate for 2 to 4 hours to pick up the color and flavor. Slicing the eggs in half will reveal a bright magenta ring on the outside, encircling a ring of white around the bright yellow yolk. The contrast is lovely. If you'd like the whites to be pink all the way through to the yolk, then leave them in the brine for 24 hours or longer. Out of the brine, the eggs will keep in a covered container in the refrigerator for about 1 week.

SPICY GOLDEN EGGS

makes 8 eggs

When friends stop by on a whim, I love having these on hand for a quick and visually striking hors d'oeuvre. I serve them cut in half with a dollop of mayonnaise and slice of the pickled jalapeño.

INGREDIENTS

1 cup/240 ml cider vinegar

Two 4-in/10-cm pieces fresh turmeric, peeled and thinly sliced, or ½ tsp ground turmeric

2 jalapeño chiles, thinly sliced

2 garlic cloves, thinly sliced

2 tsp yellow mustard seeds

1 tbsp salt

1 tbsp sugar

Eight 13-Minute Eggs (see page 28), peeled

PREPARATION

Bring the vinegar, turmeric, jalapeños, garlic, mustard seeds, salt, sugar, and 1 cup/120 ml water to a boil in a small saucepan over medium-high heat, stirring until the salt and sugar are dissolved. Remove from the heat and cool to room temperature.

Put the eggs in a container that will hold them and the pickling brine comfortably. Pour the cooled brine, solids and all, over the eggs and push them down to submerge. Cover and refrigerate for 2 to 4 hours to pick up the color and flavor. Slicing the eggs in half will reveal a golden ring on the outside, encircling a ring of white on the bright yellow yolk. The contrast is lovely. If you'd like the whites to be golden all the way through to the yolk, then leave them in the brine for 24 hours or longer. Out of the brine, the eggs will keep in a covered container in the refrigerator for about a week.

PART II.
THINGS TO PUT EGGS ON

CHAPTER 1

EGGS

on BREAD, SANDWICHES, *and such*

CARDAMOM-CORNMEAL WAFFLES WITH
EGGS, BACON, AND MAPLE SYRUP 88

EGG HOPPERS (SRI LANKAN CRÊPES)
WITH MINT SAMBAL 89

A WORKING GIRL'S SUPPER OF CRISPY
LEMON EGGS AND AVOCADO ON TOAST 92

EGGS BOURGUIGNON
(OEUFS EN MEURETTE) 93

QUAIL EGG CROSTINI THREE WAYS 97

WELSH RAREBIT WITH HIDE-AND-SEEK
EGGS AND BURNT BROCCOLI 100

CROQUE MADEMOISELLE 102

TOMATO, BACON, AND EGG TARTLETS 104

PIZZA OF THE RISING SUN 105

CHILAQUILES 112

CRAB CAKES BENNY WITH
AVOCADO CREMA 114

CARDAMOM-CORNMEAL WAFFLES WITH EGGS, BACON, AND MAPLE SYRUP

serves 4

INGREDIENTS

¾ cup/100 g all-purpose flour

¾ cup/115 g cornmeal

2 tbsp sugar

1 tsp baking powder

½ tsp salt

½ tsp ground cardamom

½ tsp ground cinnamon

2 eggs, separated

1 cup/240 ml milk

½ cup/120 ml plain yogurt or sour cream

4 tbsp unsalted butter, melted

Nonstick cooking spray

8 strips fried bacon

4 Eggs Flavorfully Basted with bacon fat
(page 60)

Grade B maple syrup, warm, for serving

PREPARATION

Arrange the oven racks in the center two positions and preheat to warm, or about 200°F/95°C.

Stir together the flour, cornmeal, sugar, baking powder, salt, cardamom, and cinnamon in a large bowl. In another bowl, lightly beat the egg yolks, then whisk in the milk, yogurt, and butter. Stir the wet mixture into the dry mixture just to combine (it should be lumpy).

Beat the egg whites with a handheld electric mixer, or in a stand mixer using the whisk attachment, to firm peaks, meaning that when the whisk is drawn from the whites a peak forms and the tip just barely curls back on itself. Gently fold the beaten whites into the batter to just incorporate.

Heat a waffle iron on medium heat. Coat with cooking spray and cook the waffles according to the manufacturer's instructions, until crisp and golden brown. You should have enough batter to make 4 waffles, so be sure to divide the batter accordingly. As the waffles are cooked, place them directly on the racks in the oven, without overlapping, to stay hot and crisp.

Serve the waffles on warmed plates with two strips of bacon crisscrossed over the center of each and a basted egg on top. Drizzle with a bit of maple syrup and pass a little extra at the table.

to drink: *coffee and orange juice*

egg tip: *Fry up the bacon while the second or third waffle is in the iron, and then transfer the bacon strips to a plate and put them in the oven to stay hot. Cook the eggs in the bacon drippings when the last waffle is in the iron.*

eGG HOPPeRS (SRI LanKan CRêPeS) WITH MINT SambaL

serves 4

INGREDIENTS

Batter

½ tsp active dry yeast

1 cup/240 ml hot tap water (105 to 115°F/
38 to 45°C)

1 tsp sugar

1½ cups/150 g rice flour

½ tsp salt

1 cup/240 ml coconut milk

Mint Sambal

1 garlic clove, smashed

¼ tsp salt

3 to 6 thin slices jalapeño chile, or to taste

1 medium shallot, coarsely chopped

⅓ cup/30 g unsweetened shredded coconut

½ cup/15 g lightly packed fresh mint leaves

Juice of 1 lime

½ tsp sugar

¼ tsp freshly ground pepper

Peanut or vegetable oil for cooking

4 room-temperature eggs

8 tbsp/75 g cooked bay shrimp (optional)

Salt and freshly ground pepper

PREPARATION

To make the batter: Sprinkle the yeast over the water and stir to dissolve. Stir in the sugar, and let stand at room temperature until foamy, 8 to 10 minutes. Whisk together the rice flour and salt in a medium bowl. Pour in the yeast mixture and whisk to a smooth, thin batter. Stir in the coconut milk, cover, and let stand at room temperature until the batter is foamy on top, about 2½ hours. If you won't be making the hoppers right away, refrigerate the batter, covered, for up to 1 day.

To make the sambal: Using a mortar and pestle, begin by pounding the garlic with the salt to a smooth paste. Continue adding the ingredients in the following order, pounding each to a coarse paste before adding the next: jalapeño, shallot, coconut, and mint. Scrape down the sides of the mortar with a rubber spatula as needed. Stir in the lime juice, sugar, and pepper and transfer the sambal to a small bowl. Alternatively, pulverize all the sambal ingredients, except the lime juice, at once in a food processor to a dry paste, then stir in the lime juice.

Arrange the oven racks in the center two positions and preheat to warm, or about 200°F/95°C. Stir the batter and add a little water, if needed, so that it is the consistency of heavy cream.

continued

Heat an 8-in/20-cm (or smaller) nonstick skillet over high heat until a droplet of water enthusiastically sizzles and evaporates almost immediately. For the first hopper, very lightly grease the skillet by wiping it with a folded paper towel that's been dipped in a bit of oil; this should be enough to cook them all. Pour in about ¼ cup/60 ml batter and quickly swirl the pan, tilting in a circular motion to coat the bottom and sides with a thin, even layer. Cover with a lid and reduce the heat to medium. Cook until the hopper is set but spongy on top and light golden brown on the bottom, with thin, crisped edges, 1½ to 2 minutes. Run a heat-proof rubber spatula around the edges and slide it out of the pan onto a wire rack or baking sheet.

Cook three more hoppers this way, but start each on medium heat. Adjust the heat as needed to avoid burning. Transfer the cooked hoppers to the oven, placing them directly on an oven rack without overlapping, while you cook the rest. The batter should yield a total of 10 hoppers, so if you mess up a couple, you should still have enough to make 4 plain and 4 with eggs.

To make the hoppers with an egg, begin as you would for the plain, swirling the batter into the bottom of the pan, but crack an egg into the center and sprinkle about 2 tbsp of the shrimp, if using, over the surface of the hopper just before covering the pan. After about 2½ minutes the hopper should be crisp on the bottom and edges, the egg white just barely set, and the yolk runny.

As the egg hoppers are cooked, slide them out of the pan directly onto small individual plates. Season the eggs with salt and pepper, and place them in the oven to stay warm until they're all ready to serve. If there's batter left, use up the rest to make more plain ones.

Top each egg hopper with a spoonful of sambal. Serve with a fork and knife and the plain hoppers rolled up to dip in the yolks. Pass the remaining sambal at the table.

to drink: *Asian beer, or tropical fruit juice at breakfast time*

egg tip: *The egg yolks should stay runny and the whites just barely set. If the whites are still a little underdone when the hopper is crisp, remove the pan from the heat but keep the lid on for another 20 to 30 seconds to finish steaming the egg.*

cook's note: *If you have a heavy granite or marble mortar and pestle, I recommend using them to make the sambal for the most authentic flavor and texture.*

EGGS ON BREAD, SANDWICHES, AND SUCH

a WORKING GIRL'S SUPPER OF CRISPY LEMON EGGS AND AVOCADO ON TOAST

serves 2

INGREDIENTS

1 tbsp extra-virgin olive oil, plus more for the bread

1½ tsp fresh lemon juice

1 green onion, white and light green parts, thinly sliced

2 fresh basil leaves, thinly sliced

Salt and freshly ground pepper

1 ripe avocado, diced

2 thick slices artisan multigrain bread

2 Crispy Fried Eggs finished with lemon juice (page 61)

Hot sauce for garnish

PREPARATION

Position an oven rack in the top slot and preheat the broiler.

Whisk together the olive oil, lemon juice, green onion, basil, and a pinch of salt and pepper in a medium bowl. Add the avocado and lightly mash it using the tines of a fork.

There's an art to this step of the process: You want the avocado to still be in chunks, but with rounded corners from the gentle mashing. The creamy mashed flesh binds the chunks together, creating two distinct textures that really make the dish.

Drizzle the bread slices with a little olive oil and place them under the broiler to toast until deeply browned, turning once, 1 to 2 minutes per side. Watch closely to avoid burning. (I place the bread directly on the oven rack, or you can put it on a baking sheet.)

Spread the toasts with the avocado mash and top each with an egg. Garnish with a sprinkle of hot sauce and serve with a fork and knife.

to drink: *a glass of rosé*

egg tip: *Fry the eggs while the bread is toasting.*

eGGS BOURGUIGNON (OeUFS en MeURETTE)

serves 4

INGREDIENTS

4 Wine-Poached Eggs (page 41), plus the poaching wine

2½ cups/600 ml homemade chicken, pork, or beef stock, or store-bought low-sodium broth

6 tbsp/85 g unsalted butter, cubed, at room temperature

1 tbsp all-purpose flour

1 tbsp light brown sugar, plus more to taste

Salt and freshly ground pepper

8 oz/225 g pearl onions, preferably red

4 oz/115 g bacon, cut into lardons (see Cook's Note, page 148)

4 oz/115 g cremini or button mushrooms

2 tsp finely chopped fresh thyme

4 thick slices baguette cut on a slight diagonal

⅓ cup/5 g lightly packed fresh parsley leaves for garnish

PREPARATION

After poaching the eggs, strain the wine through a fine-mesh strainer into a wide, heavy pot. (Transfer the eggs to a bowl of ice water and set aside.) Bring the wine to a boil over high heat and continue boiling, stirring occasionally, until it reduces to about ¼ cup/ 60 ml and coats the back of a spoon, 25 to 30 minutes. Add the stock, bring to a boil, and continue boiling until it reduces to about 1 cup/240 ml, 10 to 15 minutes.

Meanwhile, make a beurre manié by using a fork to mash together 2 tbsp of the butter and the flour in a small bowl until it is a uniform paste. When the sauce has reduced, whisk in the beurre manié and continue to cook, reducing the heat to maintain a low simmer, until the sauce thickens, about 2 minutes. Taste and add the sugar and a pinch of salt and pepper. At this point, the sauce should be quite tart and not too salty; the bacon will provide balance later. Cover the sauce and set it off the heat while you prepare the remaining ingredients. The sauce can be refrigerated for a day or two before finishing the dish.

Fill a small pot two-thirds full of water, season well with salt, and bring to a boil over high heat. Add the pearl onions (skins on) and cook until just tender but still a little firm when pierced with the tines of a fork, 6 to 8 minutes, depending on the size of the onions. Drain the onions, trim the stem and root ends, and slip off the skins and discolored outer layer; set aside.

Heat a medium, heavy pot over medium heat. Add the bacon and sauté until crispy on the edges but still fatty and meaty in the center, 5 to 7 minutes. Transfer the bacon to a medium bowl using a slotted spoon. Add the onions to the fat and sauté until evenly browned, about 5 minutes. Use the slotted spoon to transfer them to the bowl with the bacon. Pour off all but about 1 tbsp of the fat (if there are dark,

continued

burnt bits on the bottom of the pan, dump all the fat into a bowl, wipe out the pan, and add back in 1 tbsp) and melt in 1 tbsp of the butter. Add the mushrooms and sauté until they've given up their liquid and then browned, about 5 minutes. Stir in the thyme and a pinch of salt about 1 minute before the mushrooms are done. Add the bacon, onions, and sauce to the pan and bring to a low simmer. Taste and add more salt, pepper, or sugar as needed.

Meanwhile, spread the baguette slices on both sides with the remaining 3 tbsp of butter and toast in a dry skillet over medium heat until crisp and lightly browned on both sides, 1 to 2 minutes per side.

Drain the eggs from the ice water and add them to the sauce to warm through, about 1 minute. Place the toasted baguette slices on four warmed plates and put an egg on top of each. Use tongs or a slotted spoon to divide the bacon, mushrooms, and onions between the plates, arranging them around the bread, and then spoon the sauce directly over the eggs. Dot the parsley leaves about the dish to garnish before serving.

to drink: *red Burgundy, of course*

egg tip: *The key to this dish is in cooking the eggs so that the yolks are molten. When you cut into the eggs, a river of vivid yellow-orange enlivens the dish.*

Quail egg crostini three ways

makes 30 crostini

INGREDIENTS

Thirty ¼-in/6-mm slices baguette bread,
    from 1 baguette

Extra-virgin olive oil for drizzling

Salt and freshly ground pepper

**Marinated Piquillo Peppers and Onions
with Goat Cheese**

½ tsp light brown sugar

½ tsp salt

2 tbsp sherry vinegar

2 tbsp extra-virgin olive oil

7 jarred roasted piquillo peppers, sliced into
    ¼-in/6-mm strips, or 2 roasted red bell
    peppers, seeded, deribbed, and thinly sliced

½ small yellow onion, thinly sliced

2 tbsp capers, rinsed and drained

2 tbsp finely chopped fresh parsley

4 oz/115 g soft goat cheese

Grated Tomato, Olive Oil, and Spanish Ham

1 or 2 juicy, ripe tomatoes, halved crosswise

Fruity extra-virgin olive oil for drizzling

Salt

10 thin slices Spanish cured ham, such as jamón
    serrano or ibérico, or Italian prosciutto

Rare Roast Beef and Salsa Verde

½ tsp salt

2 tbsp sherry vinegar

¼ cup/60 ml extra-virgin olive oil

1 small shallot, minced

1 garlic clove, minced

Pinch of red pepper flakes

3 tbsp finely chopped fresh parsley

3 tbsp finely chopped fresh oregano

10 thin slices rare roast beef, at room temperature

30 Panfried Quail Eggs (see page 57)

PREPARATION

Preheat the oven to 375°F/190°C/gas 5.

Arrange the baguette slices on a rimmed baking sheet. Drizzle both sides lightly with oil and sprinkle with a small pinch of salt and pepper. Bake until golden brown and crisp, about 10 minutes, rotating the pan halfway through. Let the crostini cool on the baking sheet before topping and serving.

To make the marinated piquillo peppers and onions with goat cheese: Whisk to dissolve the sugar and salt in the vinegar in a medium bowl, then whisk in the olive oil. Add the peppers, onion, and capers and toss to coat well. Cover and marinate in the refrigerator

continued

overnight or at room temperature for at least 2 hours. Stir in the parsley just before serving. Spread ten of the crostini with a smear of goat cheese, then heap a spoonful of the peppers and onions (drained of their sauce) onto each.

To make the grated tomato, olive oil, and Spanish ham: Rub one side of each of ten crostini with the cut sides of the tomato, squeezing gently to leave a thin, pulpy coating. Drizzle lightly with oil and sprinkle lightly with salt. Fold a piece of ham onto each crostini.

To make the rare roast beef and salsa verde: Whisk to dissolve the salt in the vinegar in a small bowl, then whisk in the olive oil. Stir in the shallot, garlic, and pepper flakes. Stir in the parsley and oregano just before serving. Fold a slice of beef onto the remaining ten crostini and drizzle with a small spoonful of the sauce.

Top each crostini with an egg and serve.

to drink: *sherry or txakoli*

egg tip: *The eggs can be fried up to 2 hours in advance and kept at room temperature on a platter or baking sheet before assembling the crostini. They can also be made earlier on the day they will be served and refrigerated, but they are best served at room temperature, so take them out at least 1 hour before.*

WeLSH RaReBIT WITH HIDe-anD-SeeK eGGS anD BURnT BROCCOLI

serves 4

INGREDIENTS

Cheddar Sauce

2 tbsp unsalted butter

2 tbsp all-purpose flour

2 tsp yellow mustard powder

2 tsp Worcestershire sauce

½ cup/120 ml Guinness beer

Salt

⅔ cup/165 ml heavy (whipping) cream

5 oz/140 g aged white Cheddar cheese, shredded

Pinch of paprika

1½ lb/680 g broccoli crowns, cut into floret spears with 2 in/5 cm of stalk

Olive oil

Salt

4 thick slices seedy whole-grain sandwich bread

3 tbsp unsalted butter

4 room-temperature eggs

Paprika for garnish

PREPARATION

Position an oven rack about 4 in/10 cm from the top heating element and preheat the broiler.

To make the cheddar sauce: Melt the butter in a small, heavy saucepan over medium heat. When it's bubbly, whisk in the flour to form a smooth paste and cook for about 1 minute, stirring constantly. Whisk in the mustard powder and Worcestershire. Slowly pour in the beer, whisking constantly to prevent lumps from forming. Add a pinch of salt and bring the thick sauce to a simmer, stirring often. Whisk in the cream and return to a simmer, then reduce the heat to maintain a low simmer until the sauce thickens slightly, stirring often, about 5 minutes. Whisk in the cheese in two handfuls, allowing the first to completely melt before adding the second. When the cheese is melted and the sauce is rich and smooth, remove it from the heat. Taste and add the paprika and a little salt, if needed. Cover the pot and set the sauce aside.

In a large bowl, toss the broccoli with enough oil to coat very lightly and a pinch of salt. Spread out on a rimmed baking sheet and broil until charred on the edges and tender, stirring once or twice, 8 to 10 minutes. Remove from the oven and cover loosely with aluminum foil to keep hot. Leave the broiler on.

100

Meanwhile, use a cookie cutter or the lip of a drinking glass to cut a 3-in/7.5-cm circle from the center of each slice of bread. Have ready a rimmed baking sheet lined with foil, and heat a large nonstick skillet over medium-low heat. Melt 1½ tbsp of the butter in the hot skillet. When the foam subsides, add two slices of bread and toast to golden brown on one side, about 2 minutes. Fit in the cutout bread circles where you can or toast them later. Flip the bread and crack an egg into the center of each. Cover the pan, and cook until the egg whites are set on bottom but still a little underdone on top, about 2 minutes. Transfer to the baking sheet with a spatula. Melt the remaining 1½ tbsp of butter in the skillet and repeat with the remaining two slices of bread and eggs. Transfer to the baking sheet. Toast the round cutouts in the pan, if not done before.

Top the egg toasts generously with the cheese sauce to completely cover the eggs and bread. Sprinkle with paprika and broil until the cheese sauce is bubbly, about 2 minutes.

Divide the broccoli spears between four warmed plates, arranging so that the stems are pointed toward the center. Nestle a cheese-covered egg toast in the center of the broccoli ring and serve with the toasted bread rounds.

to drink: *a glass of Guinness*

egg tip: *The eggs will finish cooking under the hot sauce in the broiler, so don't worry that they are underdone in the skillet.*

Croque MaDeMoiselle

serves 4

INGREDIENTS

1 egg yolk

3 tbsp crème fraîche or 2½ tbsp sour cream thinned with ½ tbsp milk

1 tsp Dijon mustard

⅛ tsp freshly ground pepper

2 oz/55 g Gruyére cheese, shredded on the small holes of a box grater

8 thick slices brioche bread (see Cook's Note)

4 tbsp unsalted butter, at room temperature

4 thin slices country ham (about 4 oz/115 g)

4 Sunny-Side Up Eggs (see page 56)

3 tbsp minced fresh chives

PREPARATION

Preheat the oven to 350°F/180°C/gas 4.

Whisk together the egg yolk, crème fraîche, mustard, and pepper in a small bowl. Stir in the cheese and set aside.

Use a cookie cutter or the lip of a drinking glass to cut a 3-in/7.5-cm circle from the center of each slice of bread. (Save the edges to make bread crumbs or croutons.) Brush the bread circles on both sides with butter.

Working in two batches, toast them in a large, heavy skillet over medium-low heat until light golden brown and crisp on both sides, about 1 minute per side. Collect them on a rimmed baking sheet.

Top half of the toasted breads with a slice of ham and the other half with a thick coating of the cheese mixture, dividing it evenly. Unite the cheese toasts and the ham toasts to make four sandwiches. Bake until the cheese is fully melted and oozing, about 5 minutes.

Trim the straggly white edges from the cooked eggs so they fit perfectly atop each sandwich. Sprinkle with the chives and serve hot.

to drink: *Vouvray or Chardonnay*

egg tip: *To get perfectly round sunny-side up eggs, if you happen to have four 3-in/7.5-cm ring molds or ring tops for canning jars, grease the insides with butter, place them in the hot skillet, and crack the eggs inside. Then finish them in the oven.*

cook's note: *Buy a loaf of brioche that is at least 8 in/20 cm long and slice it yourself into 1-in/2.5-cm slices. If you can't find brioche, any soft artisan bread will be delicious.*

TOMATO, BACON, AND EGG TARTLETS

makes 8 tartlets

INGREDIENTS

2 sheets frozen puff pastry (from a 17.3-oz/
490-g box)

6 slices thick-cut bacon, cut into ½-in/12-mm
pieces

All-purpose flour for dusting

1 pt/280 g multicolored cherry tomatoes, halved

8 room-temperature eggs

Salt and freshly ground pepper

10 to 12 fresh basil leaves, thinly sliced

PREPARATION

Thaw the puff pastry at room temperature for 40 minutes or overnight in the refrigerator, according to the package directions. Position one rack in the upper third and another rack in the lower third of the oven and preheat to 425°F/220°C/gas 7. Line two baking sheets with parchment paper.

Meanwhile, cook the bacon in a 10-in/25-cm sauté pan or skillet over medium-high heat until crisp and browned but still a little chewy, 5 to 7 minutes. Transfer to a plate lined with a paper towel. Reserve the rendered bacon fat for brushing the edges of the tartlets.

One at a time, unfold the puff pastry sheets on a lightly floured countertop. Dust a rolling pin with flour and roll out each sheet to a 12-in/30.5-cm square, gently flattening and smoothing the surface. Cut each sheet into four squares. Arrange them about 1 in/2.5 cm apart on the baking sheets. Prick the centers of the squares several times with a fork, leaving a ¾-in/2-cm border. Divide the bacon and then the tomatoes evenly among each square, keeping the border clean. Leave a blank hole about the size of an egg yolk in the center. Brush the edges with bacon fat. Bake until the edges have risen and are light golden brown, 10 to 12 minutes, rotating the pans from front to back and top to bottom halfway through.

Remove the baking sheets from the oven. One at a time, crack the eggs into a small cup and slip them into the center of each tartlet (it's OK if some of the white drips out onto the baking sheet). Sprinkle with salt and pepper and return to the oven to finish baking until the crusts are evenly golden brown, the egg whites set, and the yolks are molten, 5 to 7 minutes, rotating the pans about halfway through. Cool a few minutes before sprinkling with basil and serving.

The tartlets will keep in the refrigerator for a few days, individually wrapped in plastic wrap. Reheat in a 350°F/180°C/gas 4 oven before serving.

to drink: *mimosas*

egg tip: *The egg yolks provide a sauce for the tartlets, so they are best served slightly thickened but still runny. Basically, just be sure not to overcook them. To check for doneness, gently shake the pan; the centers should be jiggly. They will thicken to a molten consistency as they cool.*

PIZZa OF THE RISING SUN

makes four 10- to 12-in/25- to 30.5-cm pizzas

INGREDIENTS

4 cups/500 g all-purpose flour, plus more
for dusting

2 tsp fine sea salt

¼ tsp active dry yeast

1½ cups/360 ml water

Pizza Toppings (combinations follow)

PREPARATION

Begin at least a day before you plan to bake the pizzas. Stir together the flour, salt, and yeast in a large bowl. Pour in the water and stir to form a shaggy mass. Use your hands to shape it into a gnarly ball. Cover the bowl with plastic wrap or a kitchen towel, and set aside to rise in a warm place (such as in a cupboard near the stove) until the dough has more than doubled in size and the surface is covered with small holes. This usually takes 16 to 18 hours but depends on the temperature of the room.

Scrape the dough out of the bowl onto a lightly floured countertop. Dust the top with flour and pat it into a rough square. Cut the square into four equal portions. Working with one square of dough at a time, fold in the corners to meet in the center, forming a circle. Turn the dough seam-side down and continue molding it into a smooth sphere. Dust with a little more flour and set aside. Repeat with the remaining dough to form four balls. The dough balls can be wrapped individually in plastic and refrigerated for up to 3 days.

Let the dough rest at room temperature, loosely covered with a damp kitchen towel or plastic wrap, until soft and supple, about 1 hour, or 2 hours if it was refrigerated.

Position an oven rack 4 in/10 cm from the top heating element if you have an electric oven, or 8 in/20 cm away if it's gas. Place a pizza stone on the rack. Preheat the oven to at least 500°F/260°C/gas 10, or to 550°F/290°C if it goes that high, for at least 30 minutes, preferably 1 hour, to heat the stone. Have all the toppings prepared and ready before shaping the pizzas.

Just before shaping and topping the first pizza, open the oven door for about 30 seconds (if using an electric oven only) to release some of the ambient heat, which triggers the oven to continue heating and allows the stone to get even hotter. Then, switch the oven to the broil setting (gas and electric) to preheat the broiler for cooking the pizzas.

Lightly dust the countertop with flour. Working with one ball at a time, pat the dough down and stretch it into a fat disk. Use your fingers and palms to continue pulling it wider until it's thin enough to pick up and rotate over your knuckles, gently pulling the dough and letting gravity stretch it to a 10- to 12-in/ 25- to 30.5-cm round or oval. It's most interesting slightly misshapen, so don't be meticulous about making a perfect circle. Leave some bubbles where the dough will blister in the oven, and it's totally OK to have areas where the dough is thicker or thinner.

continued

Place the dough on the edge of a lightly floured pizza peel or rimless baking sheet and quickly get to work on topping the pizza (if it's left on the peel too long, it will become difficult to slide off). Use the following toppings recipes or get creative with your own.

Here are some general guidelines for toppings: Use only about ¼ cup/60 ml of sauce per pie, spreading it almost to the edges, or start with a drizzle of olive oil on the crust if you're going sauceless; apply no more than three hefty toppings per pie so that it isn't too weighty to transfer to the oven and the crust bakes properly; finally, the eggs are always added to the pizza after it is partially baked.

Once the toppings are added, slide the pizza off the peel or baking sheet and onto the hot stone using swift, forward and back jerking motions. If adding a chicken or duck egg, broil the pizza until the crust is crisp on the bottom and lightly browned on top, 3 to 5 minutes, then remove it from the oven and quickly close the oven door to retain the heat. Carefully crack the egg in the center of the pizza to keep the yolk whole, and return it to the oven. Bake until the crust is blistered and nicely charred on top, with a few bubbly blackened areas, 1 to 3 minutes more. The cheese should be bubbly, the egg whites set and the yolks runny, and the other toppings lightly browned. For quail eggs, it will take only 30 to 45 seconds to cook the eggs under the broiler, so remove the pizza from the oven when the crust is lightly charred and the cheese is melted and beginning to bubble (basically, when it is on the verge of being done). Add the eggs, spacing them out

on the pizza, and return the pizza to the broiler until the egg whites are set and the yolks are runny.

Transfer the pizza to a cutting board. Repeat the baking process with the remaining dough. Slice the pizzas into wedges and serve with the pizza accoutrements at the table. You can bake the pizzas and serve them all at once, or bake them one at a time, taking time to enjoy each one before making the next.

to drink: *good Lambrusco*

egg tip: *Getting the timing right for baking the crust and eggs in unison may take a little practice, but you should figure it out after the first pizza. Some of the whites may ooze off the pizza and onto the pizza stone while baking. That's totally fine; just be sure to scrape it off before baking the next one.*

cook's notes: *The no-knead pizza dough method was developed by Jim Lahey and popularized in his book* My Pizza: The Easy No-Knead Way to Make Spectacular Pizza at Home. *This recipe is a slight variation from his, but the technique is the same.*

I find that a pizza baking stone is essential to making pizza in a home oven, because the crust just doesn't get crisp enough on the bottom without it. Good thing they are easy to find at kitchenware shops and many discount stores, and the small investment is totally worth the quality gained in your homemade pizzas.

pizza accoutrements to have at the table:
Pepper mill
Sea salt
Extra-virgin olive oil
Red pepper flakes
A bowl of baby arugula

coastal margherita

makes 1 pizza

INGREDIENTS

¼ cup/60 ml Pizza Sauce (page 111)

One 4-oz/115-g fresh mozzarella ball, torn into chunks

Pinch of red pepper flakes

4 to 6 salt-packed anchovy fillets, rinsed and dried

1 room-temperature hen or duck egg, or 4 quail eggs

Torn fresh basil leaves for garnish

PREPARATION

Top the pizza in this order: sauce, mozzarella, pepper flakes, and anchovies. Add the egg(s) according to the main recipe. Sprinkle with basil after baking.

pig and honey

makes 1 pizza

INGREDIENTS

Extra-virgin olive oil for brushing

2 tbsp freshly grated Pecorino Romano cheese

¼ cup/60 ml Pizza Sauce (page 111)

One 4-oz/115-g fresh mozzarella ball, torn into chunks

2 oz/55 g thinly sliced hot sopressata

1 room-temperature hen or duck egg, or 4 quail eggs

Good honey for drizzling

PREPARATION

Brush a 1-in/2.5-cm border around the edge of the dough lightly with olive oil and sprinkle the border with pecorino. Top the pizza in this order: sauce, mozzarella, and sopressata. Add the egg(s) according to the main recipe. After baking, drizzle the entire pizza (crust, too) with honey.

continued

FOReST FLOOR

makes 1 pizza

INGReDIeNTS

¼ cup/60 ml Pizza Sauce (facing page)

2½ oz/70 g Taleggio cheese, rind removed, cut into small cubes

Pinch of red pepper flakes

¼ cup/20 g very thinly sliced red onions

3 oz/85 g meaty mushrooms, such as porcini, oyster, or cremini, very thinly sliced

Extra-virgin olive oil for drizzling

Sea salt

1 hen or duck egg, or 4 quail eggs

Fresh oregano leaves for garnish

PREPARATION

Top the pizza in this order before baking: sauce, Taleggio, pepper flakes, onions, mushrooms, a drizzle of oil, and a pinch of salt. Add the egg(s) according to the main recipe. Sprinkle with oregano after baking.

aLSATIAN COUSIN

makes 1 pizza

INGReDIeNTS

Extra-virgin olive oil for drizzling

3 oz/85 g smoked mozzarella, cut into small cubes

1 garlic clove, thinly sliced

1 cup/60 g very thinly sliced Brussels sprouts or romanesco

1 slice bacon, cut into ½-in/12-mm strips

Sea salt

1 hen or duck egg, or 4 quail eggs

PREPARATION

Top the pizza in this order before baking: a drizzle of oil, mozzarella, garlic, Brussels sprouts, bacon, and a pinch of salt. Add the egg(s) according to the main recipe. Drizzle with a little more oil after baking.

pizza sauce

makes about 1 cup/240 ml

INGREDIENTS

1 cup/265 g canned whole peeled Italian plum tomatoes, preferably San Marzano, drained

½ tbsp extra-virgin olive oil

1 garlic clove, minced

Pinch of fine sea salt

PREPARATION

Squish the tomatoes with your hands in a large bowl, leaving some chunks. Stir in the oil, garlic, and salt. The sauce can be refrigerated for up to 5 days.

CHILAQUILES

serves 4

INGREDIENTS

3 large dried New Mexico chiles

Vegetable oil for deep-frying

Twelve 6-in/15-cm corn tortillas, cut into
1-by-1½-in/2.5-by-4-cm rectangles

Salt

One 14.5-oz/415-g can diced tomatoes

½ small yellow onion, coarsely chopped

3 garlic cloves, smashed

1 cup/240 ml homemade chicken or vegetable
stock or store-bought low-sodium broth

1 tsp sugar

4 room-temperature eggs

½ cup/85 g crumbled queso fresco, cotija,
or feta cheese

Mexican crema or sour cream thinned with
a splash of milk for drizzling

Garnishes and Accoutrements

Thinly sliced white or yellow onion

Thinly sliced radishes

Sliced avocado

Fresh cilantro sprigs (thin stems and leaves)

Lime wedges

Hot refried beans

PREPARATION

Slice the chiles lengthwise and discard the stem. Discard the seeds if you want mild heat, or leave them in for spicy. Tear the chiles into little pieces and put in a small bowl with the seeds, if using, and 1 cup/240 ml boiling water. Place a small dish over the top to weight them down, keeping them submerged, and rehydrate for about 20 minutes.

Meanwhile, fill a 12-in/30.5-cm cast-iron skillet with 1 in/2.5 cm oil and heat it over medium-high heat until a deep-frying ther-mometer registers 350°F/180C°C. Working in two batches, add the tortillas and fry, turning occasionally, until they're golden brown and crisp, 1 to 2 minutes. You'll know they are crisp when the vigorous bubbling ceases. Use a spider or a slotted spoon to transfer the chips to a baking sheet lined with a paper towel and season them with salt; set aside (and try not to eat them!). Leave the oil in the skillet to cool.

Position an oven rack about 4 in/10 cm from the top heating element and preheat the broiler.

Drain the chiles and combine with the tomatoes, onion, and garlic in a blender and process to a smooth purée.

When the frying oil cools a bit, pour out all but about 1 tbsp from the skillet. Reheat the remaining 1 tbsp oil over medium-high heat. When it's shimmering hot, add the chile purée (watch for splatter!) and cook, stirring almost constantly, until it has thickened slightly and the color is a bit darker red, 8 to 10 minutes. (Reduce the heat to medium if the splattering gets out of hand.) Stir in the stock, sugar, and 1 tsp salt and bring it to a boil over high heat. Reduce the heat to maintain a low simmer, cover, and cook for about 5 minutes to allow the flavors to meld.

Add the tortilla chips, tossing them gently to coat evenly with the sauce but taking care not to break them. The goal is to soften the chips so that they're still a little chewy, but certainly not mushy. Create four shallow wells in the chilaquiles and crack 1 egg into each. Sprinkle the chips and eggs with the cheese. Put the pan under the broiler until the egg whites are set, the yolks are still a little jiggly, and the chips and cheese are lightly charred in spots, about 5 minutes.

Drizzle with crema. Serve the chilaquiles from the pan at the table, with the garnishes and accoutrements in small dishes for everyone to help themselves.

to drink: *margaritas*

egg tip: *Check out the Broiled Eggs tips on pages 68–69. The eggs are best when the yolks are cooked until molten, creating a rich sauce to contrast with the spicy and acidic chilaquiles.*

CRAB CAKES BENNY WITH AVOCADO CREMA

serves 4

INGREDIENTS

⅓ cup/75 ml mayonnaise

1 egg, cold

2 tsp yellow mustard powder

1 tsp Worcestershire sauce

Pinch of cayenne pepper

1 lb/455 g cooked lump crab

2 green onions, white and light green parts, thinly sliced

1¼ cups/85 g panko bread crumbs or saltine crackers crushed into crumbs

½ avocado, coarsely chopped (see Cook's Note)

¼ cup/60 ml sour cream

1 tsp fresh lemon juice, or to taste

½ tsp salt, or to taste

4 tbsp unsalted butter

4 tbsp olive oil

8 Poached Eggs for a Crowd (page 40) or Foolproof Poached Eggs made with parsley or chives (page 44)

4 lemon wedges

Hot sauce for serving

PREPARATION

Whisk together the mayonnaise, cold egg, mustard powder, Worcestershire, and cayenne in a large bowl. Add the crab, green onions, and ½ cup/35 g of the panko and gently fold the ingredients together, taking care not to break up the chunks of crab. Cover and refrigerate for at least 30 minutes or up to 1 day.

Preheat the oven to warm, or about 200°F/95°C.

Whirl the avocado, sour cream, lemon juice, and salt in a food processor to a smooth, thick purée. Taste and adjust seasoning with lemon juice or salt; it should be quite tart to balance the richness of the crab cakes and eggs. Transfer to a bowl. If you're not serving it right away, cover with plastic wrap touching the surface and refrigerate for up to 1 day.

Form the crab mixture into 8 patties that are about 3 in/7.5 cm in diameter and ¾ in/2 cm thick. Pat both sides of each cake with a light coating of the remaining ¾ cup/50 g panko. Collect them on a baking sheet lined with waxed paper.

Heat a 12-in/30.5-cm heavy skillet, preferably cast-iron, over medium-high heat until a droplet of water enthusiastically sizzles and evaporates almost immediately. Add 2 tbsp of the butter and 2 tbsp of the oil; the butter should bubble and melt on contact. Reduce the heat to medium and add four of the crab cakes. Cook until deep golden brown and crusty on both sides, about 3 minutes per side. Use a large spatula to peek underneath to see if they are ready to flip, and turn them delicately. If the cakes are cooking unevenly, carefully rotate them around in the pan. Collect the cooked crab cakes on a second baking sheet, and put them in the oven to keep warm. Wipe out the pan with paper towels, add the remaining 2 tbsp of both butter and oil, and cook the second batch in the same manner.

Place two crab cakes on each of four warmed plates. Spoon a dollop of the avocado crema onto the center of each cake and place a poached egg on top. Serve with lemon wedges and hot sauce at the table.

to drink: *Champagne*

egg tip: *Cook the eggs while the crab cake mixture is resting in the refrigerator. Keep the hot water on the stove, and drop them back in to reheat just before serving.*

cook's note: *Chop the avocado just before it is puréed to prevent browning.*

CHAPTER **2**

EGGS on soups and STEWS

**MANTEROLA'S POZOLILLO VERDE
(GREEN POZOLE WITH CHICKEN,
FRESH CORN, AND EGGS) 118**

**SPANISH GARLIC SOUP WITH POACHED
EGGS AND PICKLED GRAPES 120**

**EGG-DROPPED MISO SOUP WITH
MUSHROOMS AND BOK CHOY 122**

**SPRING SORREL SOUP WITH TENDER
VEGETABLES AND CODDLED EGGS 124**

EGGS AND GREENS MASALA 125

**AN EARTHY STEW OF CHICKPEAS AND
SWISS CHARD WITH CRUNCHY EGGS 127**

BOUILLABAISSE OF EGGS 129

SHAKSHOUKA 131

Manterola's Pozolillo Verde (Green Pozole with Chicken, Fresh Corn, and Eggs)

serves 4

INGREDIENTS

4 cups/960 ml homemade chicken stock or store-bought low-sodium broth

1 to 1½ lb/455 to 680 g skin-on, bone-in chicken hindquarters

Salt

1 large poblano chile

1 serrano chile

8 oz/225 g tomatillos, husked, rinsed, and quartered

½ bunch fresh cilantro, stems trimmed, leaving only thin stems and leaves

¼ yellow onion, coarsely chopped

1 romaine lettuce leaf, torn into pieces

Half of a 6-in/15-cm corn tortilla, torn into pieces

2 garlic cloves, smashed

1 tbsp olive oil

2 cups/300 g fresh or frozen corn kernels

Four 5-Minute Eggs (see page 28), peeled

Garnishes

Finely shredded red cabbage

Thinly sliced radishes

Diced avocado

Fresh cilantro sprigs (thin stems and leaves)

Lime wedges

Warm corn tortillas or fried tortilla strips

PREPARATION

Bring the stock to a boil, covered in a medium saucepan, over high heat. Add the chicken and 1 tsp salt. When it returns to a boil, reduce the heat to maintain a low simmer, cover, and cook until the chicken is cooked through and easily pulls away from the bone, 35 to 40 minutes. Remove the chicken from the stock and shred it into bite-size pieces, including the skin; set aside. Keep the stock covered over low heat.

Meanwhile, position an oven rack about 4 in/10 cm from the top heating element and preheat the broiler. Place the poblano and serrano chiles on a small, rimmed baking sheet lined with aluminum foil and broil, turning occasionally, until the skins are evenly charred and the flesh is very tender, 7 to 10 minutes. Remove the chiles as they are done and put them in a bowl covered with plastic wrap to steam the skins loose. When they are cool enough to handle, peel the chiles with the aid of a paring knife, wearing plastic gloves if you have them. Seed the poblano; leave the seeds in the serrano for a spicier soup, or seed it, too, if you prefer a milder flavor.

Working in two batches, combine the chiles, tomatillos, cilantro, onion, lettuce, tortilla, garlic, 1 tsp salt, and a few tbsp stock in a blender and process to a smooth purée.

Heat the oil in a large, heavy soup pot over medium-high heat. When it's shimmering hot, stir in the green purée. When it begins to bubble and spit, reduce the heat to medium and cook, stirring constantly, until the color changes from bright green to a dull yellowish-green, 2 to 3 minutes. Add the remaining stock, pouring it into the pot through a fine-mesh strainer if it needs to be strained. Bring the soup to a boil over high heat, then reduce the heat to medium-low and simmer to meld the flavors for about 10 minutes. Add the chicken, corn, and eggs and cook just to heat through, about 5 minutes. Taste and add more salt as needed. Remove the eggs with a slotted spoon once they are warm and put them on a cutting board.

Ladle the soup into large, warmed bowls. Slice the eggs in half lengthwise and place two halves on top of each bowl of soup. Serve the cabbage, radishes, avocado, cilantro sprigs, lime wedges, and tortillas in small dishes at the table.

to drink: *Mexican beer*

egg tip: *Cook the eggs in advance, or while the chicken is simmering. Add the peeled eggs to the soup just long enough to rewarm them, but not so long that they hard-cook; you want oozing yolks, to add richness to the broth.*

cook's note: *My friend Catherine Manterola's family in central Mexico makes a special version of pozole with tomatillos and fresh corn rather than the more common hominy. This is their recipe, with an egg on top.*

SPANISH GARLIC SOUP WITH POACHED EGGS AND PICKLED GRAPES

serves 4

INGREDIENTS

¼ cup/60 ml extra-virgin olive oil

2 cups/70 g ¾-in/2-cm cubed day-old artisan white bread, crusts removed

1 cup/70 g thinly sliced leeks, white part only, rinsed and drained well

1 head garlic, peeled and thinly sliced

4 cups/960 ml homemade vegetable stock or store-bought low-sodium broth

¼ cup/30 g slivered almonds

Salt

4 Quintessential Poached Eggs (see page 38) or Foolproof Poached Eggs (see page 44)

Pickled Grapes (facing page), halved lengthwise, for garnish

PREPARATION

Heat the oil in a heavy pot over medium heat. When a bread cube sizzles enthusiastically when dropped in, add all the bread cubes and stir to coat. Cook, stirring often, until the bread cubes are evenly crisped and light golden, about 5 minutes. Reduce the heat to medium-low if they are browning too quickly or unevenly. Remove the bread cubes with a slotted spoon, leaving behind as much of the oil as possible, and set aside.

Immediately reduce the heat to medium-low, if not done before, and add the leeks and garlic. Cook, stirring often and adjusting the heat as needed to cook very slowly, until meltingly soft and fragrant, 10 to 12 minutes. Stir in the broth, almonds, 1 tsp salt, and toasted bread cubes and bring to a simmer over medium-high heat. Reduce the heat to medium-low and simmer until the bread is completely soggy, about 3 minutes.

Working in two batches, purée the soup in a blender until smooth and silky. Return the soup to a clean pot set over medium-low heat. Taste and add more salt as needed. If the soup is too thick, thin with water, adding 1 to 2 tbsp at a time. When the soup is piping hot, ladle it into warmed bowls and top with the eggs and a small spoonful of pickled grapes.

to drink: *fino sherry*

egg tip: *Keep the finished soup hot, covered, over low heat while you poach the eggs.*

PICKLED GRAPES

makes about 1 cup/155 g

INGREDIENTS

1 cup/155 g seedless grapes (green or red)

½ cup/120 ml Banyuls vinegar or sherry vinegar

½ cup/120 ml water

¼ cup/60 ml honey

1 tsp salt

PREPARATION

Prick each grape with the tines of a fork three or four times and put them in a small, heat-proof bowl or glass canning jar. Bring the vinegar, water, honey, and salt to a boil in a small saucepan over high heat, stirring to dissolve. Pour the boiling liquid over the grapes and let stand for about 1 hour to pickle. If the grapes are not completely submerged in the liquid, transfer it all to a smaller container. The grapes will keep a few days in the refrigerator, strained from the pickling liquid. (The grapes are tasty on a green salad, and the pickling liquid can be whisked with olive oil for a spectacular vinaigrette.)

EGG-DROPPED MISO SOUP WITH MUSHROOMS AND BOK CHOY

serves 4

INGREDIENTS

4 cups/960 ml dashi (see Cook's Note)

4 oz/115 g shimeji, enoki, or shiitake mushrooms, cleaned and trimmed

6 oz/170 g baby bok choy, ends trimmed and leaves separated

4 tbsp miso paste (red, white, or a combination), or to taste

4 oz/115 g silken tofu, cubed

4 Coddled Eggs (see page 31)

2 green onions, white and green parts, thinly sliced on a diagonal for garnish

PREPARATION

Bring the dashi to a boil, covered in a medium pot, over high heat. Add the mushrooms. When the dashi returns to a simmer, reduce the heat to medium and simmer until the mushrooms are just tender, about 1 minute. Use a slotted spoon to transfer them to a bowl and cover with aluminum foil to keep warm. Add the bok choy to the broth and simmer until just tender but still a little firm, about 2 minutes, then strain and transfer to a separate bowl and cover to keep warm.

Reduce the heat so the broth is just below a simmer. Put 4 tbsp miso paste into a small fine-mesh strainer and lower it into the broth. Use the back of a spoon to push the miso through the strainer and dissolve it in the broth. Remove the strainer and discard any large chunks left inside. (If your miso paste is very finely ground, then this step may not be necessary; just stir the miso directly into the broth.) Taste and add more miso as needed. Add the tofu and heat through, about 1 minute. Never allow the broth to come to a boil after the miso has been added, or it may become gritty.

Arrange the mushrooms and bok choy along the edges of four warmed soup bowls. Use a slotted spoon to divide the tofu evenly among the bowls, heaping it in the center. Make sure the broth is piping hot, then ladle it into the bowls. One at a time, peel the thick end of the eggs and slip them from the shells directly into the bowls. Garnish with green onions and serve.

variation: *For a filling meal, add a coil of cooked soba noodles to each bowl before pouring in the broth.*

to drink: *green tea*

egg tip: *Allow plenty of time for the coddled eggs to cook so they are done when the soup is ready. If the eggs are finished cooking before the soup, run cold water over them to stop the cooking, or plunge them into a bowl of ice water. They will warm up from the heat of the broth.*

cook's notes: *You will find packets of instant dashi granules at most Asian markets. I typically prefer kombu (kelp) dashi for miso soup. All you do is dissolve the granules in boiling water, similar to how you would with bouillon cubes. Substitute vegetable broth or stock only in a pinch.*

SPRING SORREL SOUP WITH TENDER VEGETABLES AND CODDLED EGGS

serves 4

INGREDIENTS

2 tbsp extra-virgin olive oil

2 medium leeks, white and light green parts, halved lengthwise and thinly sliced into half-moons, rinsed and drained well

Salt

2 garlic cloves, minced

3½ cups/840 ml homemade chicken or vegetable stock or store-bought low-sodium broth

1 large Yukon gold potato, peeled and cut into ½-in/12-mm cubes

1 large carrot, peeled, halved lengthwise, and thinly sliced into half-moons

1 medium parsnip, peeled, halved lengthwise, and thinly sliced into half-moons

1 tsp minced fresh thyme

Freshly ground pepper

3 tbsp chopped fresh herb mix, such as parsley, dill, fennel fronds, tarragon, and chives

6 oz/170 g sorrel, or spinach with a squeeze of fresh lemon juice, stemmed and coarsely chopped

4 Coddled Eggs (see page 31)

PREPARATION

Heat the oil in a large soup pot over medium-low heat. Add the leeks and a big pinch of salt and sauté until very sweet and meltingly soft, about 20 minutes. Reduce the heat to low after about 10 minutes, if needed, to keep from browning. Stir in the garlic and cook until aromatic, about 1 minute. Add the stock, potato, carrot, parsnip, thyme, a big pinch of salt, and a little pinch of pepper. Raise the heat to high to bring to a boil, then reduce to medium-low to maintain a steady simmer. Cook, stirring occasionally, until the vegetables are just tender, 10 to 12 minutes.

Stir half of the herb mix and all the sorrel into the soup; the sorrel should wilt within a few seconds. Taste and add more salt and pepper as needed.

Ladle the soup into warmed bowls and slip an egg into each. Garnish with the remaining herb mixture and serve.

to drink: *rosé*

egg tip: *To prepare the coddled eggs, pour the hot water over the eggs with forethought on the timing: You should allow plenty of time for the eggs to cook so they are done when the soup is ready to be served. If the eggs are finished cooking before the soup, run cold water over them to stop the cooking, or plunge them into a bowl of ice water. They will warm up from the heat of the broth.*

eggs and greens masala

serves 4

INGREDIENTS

4 garlic cloves

Coarse sea salt or kosher salt

1 tbsp grated peeled fresh ginger

3 tsp garam masala

2 tsp ground turmeric

Pinch of cayenne pepper

3 tbsp unsalted butter

1 tsp coriander seeds

½ tsp cumin seeds

1 large yellow onion, diced

1 tbsp hot paprika

1 lb/455 g mustard greens, thick center ribs removed, leaves torn into large pieces

One 14.5-oz/415-g can diced tomatoes

½ cup/120 ml heavy (whipping) cream

Four 5-Minute Eggs (see page 28)

Cooked basmati rice for serving

Fresh cilantro leaves for garnish

PREPARATION

Finely chop the garlic, then sprinkle it with a pinch of salt and mash to a paste with the angled edge of a knife blade, using a scraping motion against the cutting board. Stir together the garlic paste, ginger, 2 tsp of the garam masala, the turmeric, cayenne, and 1 tbsp water in a small bowl to make a paste.

Melt the butter in a Dutch oven or other large, heavy pot set over medium heat. When it's bubbly, add the coriander and cumin and toast until the butter is lightly browned, about 3 minutes. Add the onion and paprika and cook, stirring occasionally, until the onion is soft and translucent, 6 to 8 minutes. Add the masala paste and continue to sauté until the onion is very soft and lightly browned and the mixture is beginning to stick to the bottom of the pot, about 5 minutes.

Add the mustard greens in two or three batches, stirring to wilt down the leaves before each addition. When the greens are wilted, add the tomatoes and their juice, ½ cup/120 ml water, and a few big pinches of salt and bring to a simmer over medium-high heat. Reduce the heat to medium and simmer, stirring occasionally, to meld the flavors and thicken the sauce, 8 to 10 minutes.

Stir in the cream and the remaining 1 tsp garam masala. Turn off the heat and taste and add more salt as needed; add cayenne if you want more heat. Cut the eggs in half lengthwise and arrange on top of the curry, yolks up. Spoon the sauce over the eggs to heat through, but try to keep the yolks from seeping out of the whites. Use a slotted spoon to transfer the eggs to a plate. Spoon the greens and sauce over basmati rice heaped on four warmed plates. Top each with two halves of egg and garnish with cilantro before serving.

to drink: *Indian beer, such as Kingfisher*

egg tip: *In this dish, I prefer the egg yolks to be rich and gooey. Heat the eggs in the curry just long enough to warm through, but not so long that the yolks harden. If you prefer them cooked longer, that is fine, too.*

an earthy stew of chickpeas and swiss chard with crunchy eggs

serves 4

INGREDIENTS

2 tbsp extra-virgin olive oil

1 medium yellow onion, diced

1 plum tomato, diced

3 garlic cloves, minced

2 tsp chopped fresh thyme

2 cups/280 g cooked chickpeas or
    one 15-oz/430-g can chickpeas,
    drained and rinsed

2 cups/480 ml homemade chicken or vegetable
    stock or store-bought low-sodium broth

8 large Swiss chard leaves, thick center ribs
    removed, leaves coarsely chopped

¼ tsp smoked paprika, plus more to taste

Salt and freshly ground pepper

4 Crunchy Deep-Fried Eggs (see page 66) or
    Crispy Fried Eggs (see page 61)

½ cup/120 ml plain yogurt, preferably Greek style

⅓ cup/15 g chopped fresh cilantro

4 lemon wedges

PREPARATION

Heat the oil in a large soup pot over medium heat. Add the onion and sauté until tender and starting to color, about 10 minutes. Stir in the tomato, garlic, and thyme and cook until aromatic, about 2 minutes. Add the chickpeas, stock, chard, paprika, a couple of big pinches of salt, and a smaller pinch of pepper. Raise the heat to high to bring to a boil, then reduce to medium-low to maintain a steady simmer. Cook, stirring occasionally, until the chard is wilted and the flavors meld together, about 10 minutes. Taste and add more salt, pepper, or paprika as needed.

Ladle the soup into warmed bowls. Top each bowl with an egg and a big dollop of yogurt. Sprinkle with plenty of cilantro and serve with a lemon wedge.

to drink: *Rioja*

egg tip: *Keep the finished soup over low heat while you fry the eggs just before serving.*

BOUILLABAISSE OF EGGS

serves 4

INGREDIENTS

3 tbsp olive oil, plus more for brushing the bread

1 large or 2 small leeks, white and light green parts, thinly sliced, rinsed, and drained well

1 medium fennel bulb, thinly sliced with the grain, plus ¼ cup/5 g coarsely chopped fronds for garnish

8 large garlic cloves, smashed and coarsely chopped

½ cup/120 ml dry white or rosé wine

1 pt/280 g cherry or grape tomatoes, halved

2 tsp chopped fresh thyme

1 tsp finely grated orange zest

1 bay leaf

Pinch of saffron threads

Salt and freshly ground pepper

4 extra-large eggs, preferably duck eggs, cold

12 oz/340 g creamy, yellow potatoes, such as Yukon gold

8 slices baguette, cut on a diagonal

Rouille (recipe follows)

Fennel pollen for garnish (optional)

PREPARATION

Heat the oil in a medium, heavy soup pot over medium heat. When it is shimmering hot, add the leeks, sliced fennel, and garlic and toss to coat in the fat. Reduce the heat to medium-low, cover, and cook, stirring occasionally, until the vegetables are very tender and wilted, about 10 minutes.

Add the wine, raise the heat to medium-high, and bring to a boil. Cook until the wine is almost completely evaporated, 2 to 3 minutes. Pour in 3 cups/720 ml of water and add the tomatoes, thyme, orange zest, bay leaf, saffron, a few big pinches of salt, and a small pinch of pepper. Bring to a boil, then reduce the heat to maintain a low simmer. Cover, and cook until the broth is perfumed with the aromatic ingredients and the tomatoes are soft but still hold their shape, about 10 minutes. Taste and add more salt and pepper as needed (it will take quite a bit of salt to season the potatoes when they are added). Set aside ¼ cup/60 ml of broth to make the Rouille.

Meanwhile, cook the eggs according to the instructions for Quintessential Poached Eggs (see page 38), but remove them from the poaching water when they are just able to hold their shape, after about 1 minute. Very carefully transfer the delicate eggs to an ice bath.

Peel the potatoes and cut crosswise into ¼-in/6-mm slices. Add them to the broth. Return the liquid to a simmer over medium heat and cook, uncovered, until the potatoes are tender when pierced with a fork but still hold their shape, 10 to 12 minutes.

Meanwhile, preheat a stove-top grill pan over high heat. Brush both sides of the bread with oil and grill until lightly charred on both sides, 1 to 2 minutes per side.

When the potatoes are cooked, gently drop the partially poached eggs into the simmering broth so that they are completely submerged. Cover the pot, and remove it from the heat to gently finish cooking the eggs, keeping the yolks molten, 2 to 4 minutes. Be sure to remove the bay leaf before serving.

continued

Spread 4 pieces of the grilled bread with a thick smear of Rouille. Remove the eggs from the broth with a slotted spoon and place one on top of each piece of smeared bread. Taste the broth and add more salt as needed. Spoon the bouillabaisse into warmed shallow bowls, with a good heap of vegetables surrounded by broth. Nestle an egg toast on top of the vegetables. Sprinkle the chopped fennel fronds on the broth, and a pinch of fennel pollen, if using, on the eggs. Serve immediately with the extra grilled bread and rouille on the table.

to drink: *There is only one thing to drink with bouillabaisse and that is rosé from the south of France. I like Domaine Tempier.*

egg tip: *Don't attempt to strain away the thin egg whites before poaching, or the eggs will be too delicate to cook this way.*

ROUILLE

makes about ¾ cup/180 ml

INGREDIENTS

One 2-in-/5-cm-thick slice baguette, crusts removed, torn into small pieces

About ¼ cup/60 ml broth, reserved from Bouillabaisse of Eggs (preceding recipe)

1 to 2 large garlic cloves, halved lengthwise

Salt

1 large egg yolk

¼ tsp piment d'Espelette or cayenne pepper, or to taste

⅓ cup/75 ml extra-virgin olive oil

PREPARATION

Put the bread in a small bowl and add the broth, just enough to make it soggy. Using a mortar and pestle, pound the garlic and ½ tsp salt to a paste. Add the egg yolk, piment d'Espelette, and soggy bread and mash and stir briskly with the pestle until the mixture is relatively smooth and homogeneous, scraping down the sides of the mortar with a rubber spatula as needed. Very slowly drizzle in the oil, dripping it down the side of the mortar while stirring briskly with the pestle, to make an emulsified sauce. Taste and add more salt or piment d'Espelette as needed; the flavor should be intensely garlicky and a little spicy. Rouille is best used the same day.

cook's note: *You will need a mortar and pestle to prepare the rouille. (Alternatively, rouille can be made in a food processor, though the texture will be a little less alluring.)*

shakshouka

serves 4

INGREDIENTS

¼ cup/60 ml olive oil

1 large yellow onion, thinly sliced

4 garlic cloves, thinly sliced

½ tsp coriander seeds, lightly crushed with
a mortar and pestle or the back of a knife

½ tsp cumin seeds, lightly crushed with
a mortar and pestle or the back of a knife

3 bell peppers in a variety of colors, seeded,
deribbed, and cut into ½-in/12-mm strips

2 tsp light brown sugar

1 bay leaf

2 cups/530 g canned whole peeled tomatoes
and their juice

2 tsp harissa paste or 1 tsp red pepper flakes
(see Cook's Note)

Salt and freshly ground black pepper

¼ cup/10 g chopped fresh parsley, plus more
for garnish

4 room-temperature eggs

2 oz/55 g crumbled feta cheese

Warm slices of baguette or pita wedges for
serving

PREPARATION

Heat the oil in a 12-in/30.5-cm heavy skillet over
high heat. When it's shimmering hot, add the
onion and sauté until soft and just beginning to
char, about 5 minutes. Add the garlic, coriander,
and cumin and sauté until the mixture is quite
fragrant, about 1 minute more. Stir in the bell
peppers and sauté until they begin to soften
and brown, about 5 minutes. Add the sugar
and bay leaf and cook until the bell peppers
are evenly charred and tender, 3 to 4 minutes.

Add the tomatoes, ½ cup/120 ml water,
harissa, a few big pinches of salt, and a small
pinch of black pepper and bring to a simmer,
using a wooden spoon to break up the tomatoes. Reduce the heat to low and cover the pan
with a lid or a sheet of aluminum foil crimped
tightly around the edges. Stew the mixture
until the bell peppers are as tender as you'd
like, 15 to 25 minutes. I prefer them to be tender but still firm to the bite, but you may like
them very tender, as with roasted peppers.
Add a few tbsp of water, as needed, to keep the
mixture loose and saucy.

Stir in the parsley. Taste and add more salt
and black pepper as needed. Make four shallow wells in the sauce and crack an egg into
each. Adjust the heat to bring the sauce back
to a low simmer, cover, and cook until the egg
whites are just set and the yolks are still runny,
6 to 8 minutes, or longer if you prefer fully
cooked yolks.

Sprinkle on the cheese and garnish with
parsley. Dish up the shakshouka at the table,
with warm baguette slices for dipping.

to drink: *Moroccan mint tea*

egg tip: *The eggs will continue to cook off the heat,
so if you want liquid yolks, which I recommend, be
sure to pull the pan from the burner when the eggs
are still a little jiggly.*

cook's note: *Harissa paste is a fragrant and spicy
North African chile paste that can be found at specialty food stores and many supermarkets.*

CHAPTER **3**

EGGS

on SALADS

LEEKS VINAIGRETTE WITH
HERBED QUAIL EGGS 135

GRILLED ROMAINE CAESAR SALAD
WITH EGGS MIMOSA 137

BROCCOLINI, AVOCADO, AND PISTACHIO
SALAD WITH SILKY LEMON DRESSING
AND PARSLEYED EGGS 138

FRIED GREEN TOMATO SALAD WITH
SOFTLY SCRAMBLED EGGS 140

SPICY AND HERBACEOUS THAI SALAD
WITH SALTED DUCK EGGS 142

PICNIC SALAD OF WHEAT BERRIES,
FAVAS, RADISHES, AND
BEET-PICKLED EGGS 143

A NIÇOISE SALAD, OF SORTS 144

STEAK AND EGGS SALAD 146

FRISÉE AUX LARDONS AND
CRISPY BREADED EGGS 148

Leeks Vinaigrette with Herbed Quail Eggs

serves 4

INGREDIENTS

Salt

1 tbsp Champagne vinegar or white wine vinegar

1 tbsp fresh lemon juice

1 tbsp Dijon mustard

Freshly ground pepper

⅓ cup/75 ml extra-virgin olive oil

4 large or 8 small leeks

1½ tbsp capers, rinsed and drained

Six 2½-minute quail eggs (see page 27)

3 tbsp finely chopped fresh tender herbs,
    such as dill, tarragon, chervil, or parsley

PREPARATION

Fill a large pot two-thirds full of water, season well with salt, and bring to a boil over high heat.

Whisk together the vinegar, lemon juice, mustard, ¼ tsp of salt, and ⅛ tsp of pepper in a medium bowl. Slowly drizzle in the oil while whisking constantly until the dressing is fully blended. Taste and add more salt and pepper as needed. The vinaigrette should be thickened and homogenous, with a fairly strong, sour flavor that will be balanced by the sweet leeks.

Prepare the leeks by trimming the roots and dark green ends so you're left with just the light green and white parts. Cut the leeks in half lengthwise and then crosswise, so that they are each about 4 to 5 in/10 to 12 cm long. If the leek halves are wider than 1 in/2.5 cm, cut them in half again lengthwise. Rinse under cold running water, getting between the leaves to remove any dirt but keeping them intact. Tie the leeks in four bundles with kitchen twine.

When the water is boiling, add the leeks. Reduce the heat to maintain a steady simmer and cook until the leeks are very tender and sweet, 7 to 10 minutes. Drain in a colander in the sink until they are dry and cooled to just above room temperature.

Arrange the leeks on a long platter so that they are all pointing in the same direction. Pour the vinaigrette down the center of the row of leeks and sprinkle on the capers. Peel the quail eggs. Put the herbs on a small plate and, one at a time, roll the eggs in them to coat thoroughly. Slice the eggs in half lengthwise and dot on top of the leeks. Garnish with pepper and serve family-style at the table.

to drink: *Champagne*

egg tip: *If the quail eggs aren't precooked and sitting in your refrigerator waiting to be used, then they can be cooked in the boiling water before the leeks. I prefer them soft-cooked in this recipe; creamy yolks yield richness next to the tart vinaigrette. But hard-cooked are good, too.*

GRILLED ROMAINE CAESAR SALAD WITH EGGS MIMOSA

serves 4

INGREDIENTS

Croutons

2 tbsp extra-virgin olive oil

2 cups/70 g ½-in/12-mm cubed artisan bread (crusts on or off)

Salt

1 tsp minced fresh rosemary

Dressing

2 tbsp red wine vinegar

2 tbsp freshly grated Parmigiano-Reggiano cheese

1 egg yolk

2 salt-packed anchovy fillets, rinsed and dried, plus more for garnish (optional)

2 garlic cloves, smashed

½ tsp sugar

½ tsp salt

¼ tsp freshly ground pepper

¼ cup plus 2 tbsp/90 ml extra-virgin olive oil

2 heads romaine lettuce, washed and dried

1 tbsp extra-virgin olive oil

Salt

3 Grated Eggs (see page 30)

PREPARATION

To make the croutons: Heat the oil in a 10-in/25-cm sauté pan over medium heat. When a bread cube sizzles enthusiastically when dropped in, add all the bread cubes and a pinch of salt. Cook, stirring often, until crisp and golden brown, 8 to 10 minutes. Stir in the rosemary about 2 minutes before they're done.

To make the dressing: Whirl the vinegar, cheese, egg yolk, anchovies, garlic, sugar, salt, and pepper in a blender until smooth. With the blender running, slowly drizzle in the oil. Taste and add more salt and pepper as needed. The dressing can be refrigerated for up to 3 days.

Prepare a hot fire in a charcoal grill or preheat a gas grill or stove-top grill pan to high. Trim any brown spots from the root ends of the romaine heads, keeping the cores intact. Cut each head lengthwise into quarters so that each quarter is still held together by the core. Place the romaine quarters in a large bowl. Drizzle with the olive oil and sprinkle with a pinch of salt and toss to coat well. Lightly oil the grill grates using a paper towel soaked in oil and a long pair of tongs. Grill the romaine, turning to cook evenly on all sides, until lightly charred and just slightly wilted on the outside, about 2 minutes per side. The texture is best when the lettuce is lightly grilled, not overly blackened and limp.

Place two wedges of grilled romaine on each of four plates. Drizzle with a generous amount of dressing and speckle with the croutons. Sprinkle with a hefty showering of the eggs, garnish with anchovy fillets, if desired, and serve.

to drink: *Ligurian Pigato or Vermentino*

egg tip: *Grate the eggs before grilling the lettuce.*

BROCCOLINI, AVOCADO, AND PISTACHIO SALAD WITH SILKY LEMON DRESSING AND PARSLEYED EGGS

serves 4

INGREDIENTS

1½ lb/680 g broccolini, tough ends trimmed

2 tsp extra-virgin olive oil plus ½ cup/120 ml

Salt and freshly ground pepper

1½ tbsp fresh lemon juice plus 1 tsp finely grated zest

1 tbsp Moscatel vinegar or another good wine vinegar, such as Banyuls

1 tsp honey

½ tsp Dijon mustard

1 egg yolk

1 avocado, diced

⅓ cup/45 g roasted unsalted pistachios

2 tbsp minced fresh chives

¼ cup/10 g finely chopped fresh parsley

Four 5-Minute Eggs (see page 28), at room temperature

PREPARATION

Preheat the oven to 450°F/230°C/gas 8.

Toss the broccolini in a large bowl with the 2 tsp of oil and a big pinch of salt and a smaller pinch of pepper. Spread out on a rimmed baking sheet and roast, turning once or twice, until the stalks are just tender but still firm and the florets are lightly charred, 5 to 7 minutes. Let the broccolini cool while you make the dressing.

Whirl the lemon juice and zest, vinegar, honey, mustard, egg yolk, and a big pinch of salt in a blender until smooth. With the blender running, slowly drizzle in the remaining ½ cup/120 ml of oil through the hole in the lid and process until smooth and silky. Taste and add more salt as needed.

When the broccolini is cooled to room temperature (or it can still be a just a little warm), transfer it to a large bowl and add the avocado, pistachios, and chives. Toss with enough of the dressing to coat well (reserve any extra dressing for another use). Divide the salad between four plates. Put the parsley on a small plate and, one at a time, roll the eggs in it to coat thoroughly. Put an egg on top of each salad and garnish with freshly ground pepper. For a dramatic presentation, cut a small slit in the side of each egg to let the yolk begin to flow out just before serving.

to drink: *Chablis*

egg tip: *Cook and cool the eggs in advance or while the broccolini is roasting.*

FRIED GREEN TOMATO SALAD WITH SOFTLY SCRAMBLED EGGS

serves 4

INGREDIENTS

Fried Green Tomatoes

¼ cup/30 g all-purpose flour plus 2 tbsp

1 egg

¼ cup/60 ml buttermilk

⅓ cup/50 g cornmeal

Salt and freshly ground pepper

2 medium firm, underripe green tomatoes, cut into ⅓-in-/8-mm-thick slices

Vegetable oil for frying

Tomato Salad

1½ tbsp extra-virgin olive oil

2 tsp red wine vinegar

Salt and freshly ground pepper

8 oz/225 g ripe heirloom tomatoes in a variety of colors, cut into bite-size wedges

⅔ cup/85 g halved cherry tomatoes

¼ cup/25 g thinly sliced shallots

2 tbsp fresh chives cut into 1-in/2.5-cm lengths

4 Scrambled Eggs, the French Way (see page 50)

2 tbsp minced fresh chives

Tabasco sauce for serving (optional)

PREPARATION

To make the fried green tomatoes: Set up an assembly line with one shallow dish containing the ¼ cup/30 g of flour; a second dish with the egg and buttermilk whisked together; and a third dish with the cornmeal, the remaining 2 tbsp of flour, a big pinch of salt, and a small pinch of pepper mixed together.

Generously season the green tomatoes with salt and pepper. Coat a tomato piece on both sides with a thin film of flour. Then dip in the egg mixture and shake off the excess. Finally, coat in the cornmeal mixture, patting it in. Do this with all the green tomato pieces, and collect them on a rimmed baking sheet.

Heat a large skillet, preferably cast-iron, filled with ¼ in/6 mm of oil over medium-high heat. The oil is hot enough when a small crumb of breading bubbles steadily and starts to turn golden brown within 30 seconds. Carefully drop the tomatoes into the hot oil, working in batches if necessary, and fry until crisp and golden brown on both sides, 2 to 3 minutes per side. Remove the tomatoes as they are done and place them on paper towels. Sprinkle with salt and set them aside to cool.

To make the tomato salad: Whisk together the oil, vinegar, and a pinch of salt and pepper in a large bowl. Just before serving, add the heirloom and cherry tomatoes, shallots, and chives and toss to coat. Taste and add more salt and pepper as needed.

Heap the salad in the center of a large platter. Overlap the fried green tomatoes over the salad. Pour the scrambled eggs in a heap over the fried tomatoes, scatter the minced chives on top, and serve family-style with Tabasco, if desired.

to drink: *Italian rosé*

egg tip: *Get the eggs out of the pan right when they're cooked to perfection.*

SPICY AND HERBACEOUS THAI SALAD WITH SALTED DUCK EGGS

serves 2

INGREDIENTS

2 tbsp coconut milk

1½ tbsp fresh lime juice, preferably from Key limes

1 tbsp Thai fish sauce

2 tsp finely chopped palm sugar or light brown sugar (see Cook's Note)

1 large stalk thinly sliced lemongrass, tender parts from the center only

1 large garlic clove, minced

1 fresh Thai chile, preferably red, or small seeded serrano chile, thinly sliced

1 cup/30 g lightly packed torn green lettuce leaves

¼ cup/40 g julienned carrots

¼ cup/40 g julienned parsnips

¼ cup/10 g lightly packed coarsely chopped cilantro

2 green onions, white and green parts, thinly sliced on a severe diagonal

2 tbsp coarsely chopped roasted unsalted peanuts or cashews

1 Salted Duck Egg (see page 77) or 13-Minute Egg (see page 28), chopped

1½ tbsp very thinly sliced fresh Thai basil

PREPARATION

Heat the coconut milk, lime juice, fish sauce, sugar, lemongrass, garlic, and chile in a wok or 10-in/25-cm skillet over medium heat, stirring to dissolve the sugar, just until the dressing is warm to the touch, less than 1 minute.

Add the lettuce, carrots, parsnips, cilantro, green onions, and nuts and toss very briefly but thoroughly in the warmed dressing. Divide the salad, liquid and all, between two plates. Sprinkle with the chopped egg, then the Thai basil, and serve.

to drink: *Thai drinking vinegar mixed with soda water and a squeeze of lime. (I prefer the Som brand of Thai-style drinking vinegars, available online at www.pokpoksom.com.)*

egg tip: *The eggs can be cooked well in advance of preparing the salad, but it's best to chop them just before serving.*

cook's note: *Palm sugar is a caramel-colored natural sweetener that comes dried in solid discs. It's available at Asian markets and some specialty grocery stores.*

PICNIC SALAD OF WHEAT BERRIES, FAVAS, RADISHES, AND BEET-PICKLED EGGS

serves 4

INGREDIENTS

1¼ cups/230 g wheat berries, kamut, or spelt

Salt

2 lb/910 g fava beans

1 tbsp fresh lemon juice

1 tbsp golden or white balsamic or sherry vinegar

1 tsp honey

Freshly ground pepper

3 tbsp extra-virgin olive oil

5 or 6 radishes, very thinly sliced

3 green onions, white and green parts, thinly sliced

3 oz/85 g crumbled feta cheese

3 tbsp thinly sliced fresh mint

3 cups/75 g lightly packed baby arugula leaves for serving

4 Beet-Pickled Eggs (see page 80), thinly sliced or cut into wedges, plus the pickled beets

PREPARATION

Soak the wheat berries in 4 cups/960 ml water for at least 4 hours, preferably overnight.

Drain the wheat berries and put them in a medium pot with 5 cups/1.2 L water and a few big pinches of salt. Bring to a boil over high heat. Reduce the heat to maintain a low simmer, cover, and cook until the grains are pleasantly chewy, 50 minutes to 1 hour. When a few float and appear to have burst open, you can bet the rest are done. Drain and rinse under cold running water to cool. Pour the grains onto a kitchen towel to dry.

Bring 4 cups/960 ml water to a boil in a medium saucepan over high heat. Snap the stem ends off the beans and peel away the stringy seams on either side of the pod. Pull open the pods and remove the beans inside. Drop the beans in the boiling water for 30 seconds, then drain and immediately plunge them into a bowl of ice water for a few minutes to stop the cooking. When cooled, tear the outer shell with your fingernail and pinch out the bright green beans inside. Discard the shells.

Whisk together the lemon juice, vinegar, honey, ½ tsp salt, and a big pinch of pepper in a large bowl. Slowly drizzle in the oil while whisking constantly until the dressing is fully blended.

Add the cooled wheat berries, fava beans, radishes, and green onions to the bowl with the vinaigrette and toss to coat well. Add the feta and mint and gently toss. Taste and add more salt and pepper as needed. The flavor will be best after the salad is refrigerated for a few hours. It will keep up to 2 days.

To serve, spoon the salad over a bed of arugula leaves in shallow bowls. Top each with a few slices of pickled beets and an egg.

to drink: *Bugey Cerdon, or another bubbly pink French wine*

egg tip: *Make the eggs up to 1 week ahead.*

a niçoise salad, of sorts

serves 4

INGREDIENTS

Tuna Sauce

One 5-oz/140-g jar tuna packed in olive oil, drained, plus 1 tbsp of the oil (see Cook's Note, page 191)

¼ cup/60 ml mayonnaise

2½ tsp fresh lemon juice

½ tsp salt

Salad

1 lb/455 g red or yellow waxy potatoes

Salt

7 oz/200 g fresh green beans, preferably haricots verts

7 oz/200 g red heirloom tomatoes, cut into ¾-in/2-cm chunks (seeded if they're especially juicy)

1½ cups/40 g lightly packed tender greens, such as watercress, spinach, or baby arugula

¼ cup/35 g pitted Niçoise olives

¼ cup/10 g finely chopped fresh parsley

1 tbsp capers, rinsed and drained

2½ tbsp extra-virgin olive oil

2½ tsp fresh lemon juice

Freshly ground pepper

Four 6-Minute Eggs (see page 28)

8 salt-packed anchovy fillets, rinsed and dried

PREPARATION

To make the tuna sauce: Whirl the tuna and reserved oil, the mayonnaise, lemon juice, and salt in a food processor to a smooth purée. Taste and add more salt as needed. The sauce can be refrigerated for up to 2 days.

To make the salad: Put the potatoes in a medium pot and fill it with enough water to cover them by at least 2 in/5 cm. Add a few big pinches of salt and bring to a boil over high heat. Reduce the heat to maintain a steady simmer, and cook the potatoes until tender when pierced with a wooden skewer or the tines of a fork, 15 to 25 minutes, depending on their size. Remove the potatoes from the water as they are done, transferring them to a kitchen towel to cool and dry. When they're cool enough to handle, peel (if you'd like), and cut them into ¾-in/2-cm chunks. Put the potatoes in a large mixing bowl and set aside.

Cook the beans in a medium pot of boiling salted water until they're tender but still a bit crisp and very bright green, about 3 minutes. Drain well and then transfer to a bowl of ice water to stop the cooking. When cool, remove the beans from the water, blot dry, and add them to the bowl with the potatoes, along with the tomatoes, greens, olives, parsley, and capers.

Whisk together the olive oil, lemon juice, a heaping ½ tsp salt, and ¼ tsp ground pepper in a small bowl. Drizzle the salad mixture with the dressing and toss gently to coat, taking care not to break up the potatoes. Taste and add more salt and pepper as needed.

On each of four chilled plates, smear 2 tbsp of the tuna sauce in a big circle in the center of the plate, as if you were spreading sauce on a pizza. Heap a portion of the salad in the center of the sauce. Tear the eggs in half crosswise and nestle two halves, yolk-side up, on top of each salad. Crisscross 2 anchovy fillets over the top, and garnish with freshly ground pepper. Serve immediately.

to drink: *Provençal rosé*

egg tip: *The eggs can be cooked a few days before making the salad. Or cook them in the pot of water for the green beans, just before cooking the beans.*

steak and eggs salad

serves 4

INGREDIENTS

1 lb/455 g flatiron, flank, or hanger steak

3 oz/85 g wedge blue cheese, like Stilton, Fourme d'Ambert, or Rogue River Blue, cut into 4 thin slices

Salt and freshly ground pepper

3 tbsp extra-virgin olive oil, plus more for rubbing the steak

1 tbsp good aged balsamic vinegar, plus more for drizzling

1 small red onion, cut into ¾-in/2-cm wedges

2 fresh rosemary sprigs

5 oz/140 g baby arugula

4 Wine-Poached Eggs (see page 41), Breaded Eggs (see page 67), or Quintessential Poached Eggs (see page 38)

PREPARATION

Set both the steak and the cheese out at room temperature for 30 minutes to 1 hour before cooking. Season the steak well with salt and pepper on both sides.

Preheat the oven to 450°F/230°C/gas 8.

Whisk together the oil, vinegar, ½ tsp salt, and a pinch of pepper in a large bowl. Toss the onion wedges in the dressing, breaking them apart. Use a slotted spoon to transfer the onion from the dressing to a rimmed baking sheet, trying to reserve as much dressing as possible in the bowl; you should be left with at least 1 tsp. Spread out the onion, strew the rosemary sprigs over the top, and sprinkle

with another pinch of salt. Roast, stirring once, until the onions are tender and charred at the tips, about 15 minutes. Discard the rosemary and let the onion cool while you cook the steak.

Prepare a hot fire in a charcoal grill or preheat a gas grill or stove-top grill pan to high.

Rub the steak with just enough oil to very lightly coat. When the grill is smoking hot, lightly oil the grill grates using a paper towel soaked in oil and a long pair of tongs, and add the steak. Cook, without moving, until deeply charred grill marks form, 2 to 3 minutes, then rotate the steak a quarter turn to create a crosshatch pattern and grill 2 to 3 minutes more. If it's charring too quickly, reduce the heat to medium-high or move the steak to a slightly cooler area of the grill. Flip the steak and continue cooking to medium-rare, or warm and mostly red with a line of pink between the center and the outside, which should take 3 to 6 minutes more. I test the doneness of steaks by inserting a thin-tined meat fork or metal cake tester in the thickest part of the meat and letting it sit for a few seconds to allow the heat to conduct. Then I touch it to my upper lip (which is very heat sensitive, and so is yours) to see what the internal temperature feels like. For medium-rare, it should be warm; you should be able to leave the metal against your skin without needing to pull it away. If you prefer a medium steak, then let it cook until the center is a little warmer, but not hot. When the metal is hot, the steak is certainly medium-well to well done. If that is how you like it, then begin the steak on a medium grill to avoid burning the outside.

When the steak is cooked to your liking, transfer it to a cutting board, crosshatch-side up, and let rest for 5 minutes or so before thinly slicing it against the grain.

Just before serving, add the arugula and roasted onions to the bowl with the vinaigrette and toss to coat. Taste and add more salt and pepper as needed. Fan a quarter of the steak onto one side of each of four plates. Mound a portion of the salad on the other side, slightly overlapping the steak. Place an egg in the center of each salad and drape a slice of cheese to partially cover the steak and greens. Drizzle the steak with a little balsamic, garnish with pepper, and serve.

to drink: *Barbera d'Alba*

egg tip: *For poached eggs, cook them while the steak is resting off the grill. For breaded eggs, poach and bread them in advance, and then fry them while the steak rests.*

FRISÉE AUX LARDONS AND CRISPY BREADED EGGS

serves 4

INGREDIENTS

2 heads frisée or curly endive, dark green leaves trimmed, cored, cut into large bite-size pieces

1 tbsp olive oil

6 oz/170 g bacon, cut into lardons (see Cook's Note)

1 tbsp plus 2 tsp sherry vinegar

Salt and freshly ground pepper

¼ cup/10 g very coarsely chopped fresh tender herbs, such as chives, tarragon, parsley, and dill

4 Breaded Eggs (see page 67) or Quintessential Poached Eggs (see page 38)

PREPARATION

Put the frisée in a large bowl next to the stove.

Heat the oil in a small skillet over medium-high heat. When it's shimmering hot, add the bacon and sauté until crispy on the edges but still fatty and meaty in the center, 3 to 5 minutes. Pour the bacon and all its rendered fat over the frisée and toss to coat and wilt the greens. Add the vinegar and a pinch of salt and pepper and toss until well combined. Gently toss in the herbs.

Mound a portion of the salad in each of four shallow bowls and top with the eggs. Garnish with a few grinds of pepper and serve right away.

to drink: *Beaujolais*

egg tip: *Before cooking the bacon, poach and cool the eggs, then bread them. Have the oil for deep-frying hot and waiting. If you're up for it, fry the breaded eggs while the bacon is cooking so both will be hot and ready at the same time. You could also fry the bacon first, and then the eggs while you're tossing and plating the salad.*

cook's note: *For lardons, bacon or pancetta is cut against the grain into little rectangular strips. I like lardons to be about 1 in/2.5 cm long and ½ in/12 mm thick, for tender yet crispy chunks of smoky pork belly, which you won't get with presliced bacon. So buy an unsliced slab of bacon at the butcher counter and cut it yourself. Otherwise, the dish will still be delicious if you use presliced bacon, just be sure not to cook it to the point that it is super-crispy and dry.*

CHAPTER 4

EGGS
on VEGETABLES

CRUSHED POTATOES WITH CHORIZO,
EGGS, AND GREEN CHILE SALSA 152

RED FLANNEL HASH WITH FRIED EGGS
AND HORSERADISH CREAM 155

SUMMER SUCCOTASH WITH
CREAMY SIMMERED EGGS 157

CHARRED RAPINI WITH
GARLIC-CHILE EGGS 158

ROASTED ASPARAGUS WITH
CREAMED LEEKS, MORELS, AND
POPPY SEED EGGS 160

GRILLED SPRING ONIONS WITH
HAZELNUT ROMESCO AND
OLIVE OIL EGGS 162

STIR-FRIED BRUSSELS SPROUTS
AND WOK-FRIED EGGS 165

MISO-CREAMED KALE AND MUSHROOMS
WITH SOY SAUCE EGGS 166

CRUSHED POTATOES WITH CHORIZO, EGGS, AND GREEN CHILE SALSA

serves 4

INGREDIENTS

1 lb/455 g baby yellow potatoes (about 1½ to 2 in/4 to 5 cm in diameter)

Salt

4 tbsp/60 ml olive oil

7 oz/200 g fresh chorizo, casings removed (see Cook's Note)

½ large yellow onion, diced

4 room-temperature eggs

¼ cup/5 g very coarsely chopped fresh cilantro, including thin stems and leaves

1 cup/85 g shredded Cheddar cheese

Green Chile Salsa (facing page)

PREPARATION

Put the potatoes in a medium pot and fill it with enough water to cover them by at least 2 in/5 cm. Add a few big pinches of salt and bring to a boil over high heat. Reduce the heat to maintain a steady simmer, and cook the potatoes until tender when pierced with a skewer or a fork, 7 to 10 minutes. Drain the potatoes well. While still warm, gently smash the potatoes between your hands, flattening into cakes that are about ½ in/12 mm thick. Try to keep them intact, but it's OK if some crumble apart. Cool to room temperature.

Preheat the oven to 400°F/200°C/gas 6.

Heat 2 tbsp of the oil in a 12-in/30.5-cm skillet, preferably cast-iron, over medium-high heat. Add the chorizo and onion and cook, breaking up the chorizo and stirring often, until the meat is cooked through and crusty and the onion is tender and lightly charred, 8 to 10 minutes. Transfer the chorizo mixture to a small bowl and cover to keep warm. Wipe out the skillet with a paper towel. Add the remaining 2 tbsp of oil and place over medium heat. When it's shimmering hot, add the potatoes and cook, carefully turning once, until crispy on both sides, 8 to 10 minutes.

Meanwhile, fry the eggs according to the instructions for Sunny-Side Up Eggs (see page 56), but just until they are set on the bottom but still runny on top.

Divide the potatoes between four plates. Toss half of the cilantro with the chorizo mixture and spoon it over the potatoes. Top each serving with an egg and sprinkle with cheese. Place the plates in the oven until the cheese is melted and the eggs are cooked through, about 5 minutes. Top each with a big spoonful of the salsa and the remaining cilantro and serve.

to drink: *Agua fresca or Mexican beer*

egg tip: *Cook the eggs just until they are set enough to safely transfer from the pan to the plates. They will continue cooking in the oven, and you want them to be molten and oozing when cut into.*

cook's note: *Purchase fresh chorizo for this dish, rather than dry-cured. It's sold at Mexican markets and most supermarkets.*

Green chile salsa

INGREDIENTS

6 oz/170 g tomatillos, husked and rinsed

2 Anaheim chiles

1 jalapeño chile (optional; do not use if you prefer mild salsa)

2 garlic cloves, unpeeled

1 tsp sugar

½ tsp salt

¼ yellow onion, finely chopped

3 tbsp chopped fresh cilantro

PREPARATION

Position an oven rack about 4 in/10 cm from the top heating element and preheat the broiler. Spread out the tomatillos, the Anaheim and jalapeño chiles, and the garlic on a rimmed baking sheet lined with aluminum foil. Broil, turning once, until the skins are evenly charred and the flesh is very tender, 7 to 10 minutes. When the chiles are cool enough to handle, peel the skins but don't be meticulous about it; a little char in the salsa is a good thing. Stem and seed the chiles and peel the garlic and put them in a blender with the tomatillos and their juices, sugar, salt, and ¼ cup/60 ml water. Process until the salsa is a smooth purée. Rinse the onion under cold water, then drain well and stir into the salsa along with the cilantro in a medium bowl. (Taste and add more sugar and salt as needed.) Refrigerate to cool. The salsa tastes best a few hours after it is made.

Red Flannel Hash with Fried Eggs and Horseradish Cream

serves 4

INGREDIENTS

8 oz/225 g medium red beets

½ cup/120 ml sour cream

1 tbsp plus 1 tsp prepared horseradish

1 tsp fresh lemon juice

Salt

12 oz/340 g sweet potatoes, peeled and cut into ¾-in/2-cm chunks

12 oz/340 g red potatoes, unpeeled and cut into ¾-in/2-cm chunks

4 tbsp/60 ml vegetable oil

1 small red onion, thinly sliced

4 oz/115 g sliced pastrami or corned beef, cut into ¾-in/2-cm pieces

1 cup/15 g lightly packed fresh parsley leaves

4 Panfried Eggs (see page 56), cooked to your liking

Freshly cracked black pepper for garnish

PREPARATION

Preheat the oven to 375°F/190°C/gas 5. Wrap the beets individually in aluminum foil and roast on a rimmed baking sheet until tender when pierced with a fork, 1 to 1½ hours, depending on their size. When they are cool enough to handle, peel the beets with the aid of a paring knife and a paper towel, rubbing the skin away from the flesh, and cut them into ¾-in/2-cm chunks. (Wear rubber gloves if you have them to protect your hands from staining.)

Meanwhile, stir together the sour cream, horseradish, lemon juice, and ½ tsp salt in a small bowl. Taste and add more salt as needed. Cover and refrigerate until you're ready to serve.

Put the sweet potatoes and red potatoes in a medium pot and fill it with enough water to cover them by at least 2 in/5 cm. Add a few big pinches of salt and bring to a boil over high heat. Reduce the heat to maintain a steady simmer, and cook the potatoes until tender when pierced with a wooden skewer or a fork, 5 to 8 minutes. Drain the potatoes well and place on a kitchen towel to cool and dry.

Heat 2 tbsp of the oil in a 12-in/30.5-cm skillet, preferably cast-iron, over medium-high heat until it just begins to smoke. Add the onion and sauté until tender and evenly browned on the edges, about 6 minutes. Season with salt and transfer the onion to a small bowl.

continued

Heat the remaining 2 tbsp of oil in the same pan. When it just begins to smoke, add the potatoes and beets and toss to coat in the oil, then spread them out in the pan in a single layer. Let the vegetables cook on one side, without moving, to develop a crust, about 2 minutes. Add the pastrami and continue cooking, gently turning the vegetables, until they are evenly browned and crusty, about 6 minutes. Mix in the onion and continue cooking until heated through, about 1 minute. Remove the pan from the heat and stir in the parsley. Taste and add more salt as needed.

Smear a heaping tablespoonful of the horseradish cream in a crescent-moon shape on four plates. Spoon a quarter of the hash in a low heap in the center of each plate, so that some of the horseradish cream is still exposed. Top with an egg, garnish with a little cracked black pepper, and serve.

to drink: *hard cider*

egg tip: *Start heating the skillet for the eggs just after the pastrami is added to the hash, so that they will be done at about the same time. Or cover the finished hash to keep it hot while you fry the eggs.*

SUMMER SUCCOTASH WITH CREAMY SIMMERED EGGS

serves 4

INGREDIENTS

2 ears sweet corn, shucked

1 tbsp extra-virgin olive oil

3 oz/85 g thick-cut bacon,
    cut into ½-in/12-mm strips

1 medium yellow onion, diced

8 oz/225 g zucchini, cut into ½-in/12-mm cubes

8 oz/225 g green beans, cut on a diagonal into
    ¾-in/2-cm pieces

1 cup/240 ml homemade chicken or vegetable
    stock or store-bought low-sodium broth

1 plum tomato, diced

Salt

Freshly ground pepper

⅓ cup/75 ml sour cream

1½ tbsp chopped fresh herbs, such as oregano,
    basil, and thyme

4 room-temperature eggs

Corn bread for serving

Hot sauce for serving

PREPARATION

Cut the corn kernels off the cobs into a large bowl. Use the spine of the knife to scrape out any remaining corn juice from the cob into the bowl; set aside.

Heat the oil in a wide shallow pot over medium-high heat. When it's shimmering hot, add the bacon and fry until crispy, about 5 minutes. Use a slotted spoon to transfer the bacon to a plate lined with a paper towel. Add the onion to the fat in the pan and sauté until translucent and golden brown at the edges, about 8 minutes. Add the corn and its juice, the zucchini, and beans and sauté until the beans are bright green and all the vegetables just begin to reveal their sweet flavor and tenderness, about 5 minutes.

Add the stock, tomato, 1 tsp salt, and ¼ tsp pepper. Bring the mixture to a boil, cover, and reduce the heat to medium to maintain a low simmer and cook until the vegetables are crisp-tender, 6 to 8 minutes. Stir in the cooked bacon, sour cream, and herbs. Taste and add more salt and pepper as needed.

Make four shallow wells in the succotash and crack an egg into each. Cover and gently simmer until the egg whites are cooked through and the yolks are still molten, 7 to 9 minutes. Spoon a serving of the succotash and an egg into each of four warmed bowls. Serve with corn bread and hot sauce at the table.

to drink: *Muscadet*

egg tip: Make sure the succotash is at a low simmer and keep the pan covered tightly, so that the tops of the eggs are steamed while the bottoms are gently coddled in the liquid. The eggs can be cooked a few minutes longer if you prefer firm yolks.

CHARRED RAPINI WITH GARLIC-CHILE EGGS

serves 2 as a main or 4 as part of a larger meal

INGREDIENTS

1 lb/455 g rapini (see Cook's Note)

2 tbsp olive oil, plus more for drizzling

1 tbsp balsamic vinegar

Salt and freshly ground pepper

4 thick slices artisan bread (optional)

4 Garlic-Chile Eggs (see page 62)

4 lemon wedges (optional)

PREPARATION

Prepare a hot fire in a charcoal grill or preheat a gas grill or stove-top grill pan to medium-high.

Trim the dried-out ends and any brown or shriveled leaves from the rapini and discard. Wash and dry the rapini very well. Toss the rapini in a large bowl with the oil, vinegar, a big pinch of salt, and a smaller pinch of pepper. Marinate at room temperature for 15 to 20 minutes while you're waiting for the grill to heat up.

Lightly oil the grill grates using a paper towel soaked in oil and a long pair of tongs. Strew the rapini about the grill and cook, turning occasionally, until evenly charred in spots and the thickest stalks are tender when pierced with a wooden skewer or a fork, 3 to 5 minutes. Transfer the grilled rapini to a platter as it's done and cover loosely with aluminum foil to keep warm.

Drizzle both sides of the bread, if using, with olive oil and grill until charred with marks from the grill, turning once, about 1 minute per side.

Slide the eggs on top of the platter of rapini. Drizzle the greens with another glug of olive oil and sprinkle with a little more salt, if needed. Serve with the bread and lemon wedges, if desired.

to drink: *Peroni beer*

egg tip: *This dish can be cooked alfresco all the way, because the eggs can be fried in a skillet set directly on the grill grates. Do this after grilling the rapini and bread. You may want to brush the grill clean first.*

cook's note: *Rapini is also called broccoli raab or rabe and it can be found year-round at many supermarkets, and at farmers' markets from fall through spring. Broccolini is a good substitute, but it doesn't have the bushy leaves.*

ROASTED ASPARAGUS WITH CREAMED LEEKS, MORELS, AND POPPY SEED EGGS

serves 2

INGREDIENTS

1 lb/455 g asparagus

Extra-virgin olive oil for the asparagus

Salt and freshly ground pepper

6 oz/170 g morel mushrooms, cleaned and trimmed

1 tbsp unsalted butter

1 small leek, white and light green parts, halved lengthwise and thinly sliced into half-moons, rinsed, and drained well

¼ cup/60 ml dry white wine

¼ cup/60 ml heavy (whipping) cream

2 Foolproof Poached Eggs (see page 44), coated in poppy seeds

PREPARATION

Preheat the oven to 400°F/200°C/gas 6.

Trim the asparagus and peel the bottom half of the stalks if they're a bit tough. Toss the asparagus in a large bowl with enough oil to lightly coat and a big pinch of salt and a smaller pinch of pepper. Spread out on a rimmed baking sheet and roast until crisp-tender, 8 to 12 minutes, depending on their thickness.

Fill a medium pot with 4 cups/960 ml of water, season well with salt, and bring to a boil over high heat. Reduce the heat to medium-high to maintain a steady simmer. Add the morels and cook for 30 seconds, then drain in a colander, reserving about ¼ cup/60 ml of the water. When they're cool enough to handle, gently squeeze the mushrooms in paper towels or a kitchen towel to remove excess water. Spread them out on a kitchen towel to continue drying and cooling while you begin the sauce.

Melt the butter in a small sauté pan or skillet over medium heat. When it's bubbly, add the leek and cook, stirring occasionally, until soft, about 5 minutes. Add the white wine and simmer until almost dry, 1 to 2 minutes. Add the cream, morels, and a pinch of salt and bring to a steady simmer over medium-high heat. Reduce the heat to medium and cook at a gentle simmer until the sauce turns a very light shade of green and is slightly thickened, 1 to 2 minutes. If it becomes too thick, thin with a splash of the reserved mushroom water. Taste and add more salt as needed.

Divide the asparagus between two warmed plates, arranging them so that the tips are all pointing in the same direction. Spoon the sauce over the center of the stalks. Place an egg on top and serve.

to drink: *Sancerre or Pouilly-Fumé*

egg tip: *Poach the eggs, and then cool them in an ice bath, keeping them in the plastic wrap. Just before serving, drop them back into a pot of slowly simmering water to rewarm, then unwrap.*

GRILLED SPRING ONIONS WITH HAZELNUT ROMESCO AND OLIVE OIL EGGS

serves 4

INGREDIENTS

Romesco Sauce

1 dried ancho chile (sometimes called pasilla)

⅓ cup/85 g canned diced tomatoes

2 tbsp sherry vinegar

¼ cup/40 g roasted hazelnuts

2 garlic cloves

1 roasted red bell pepper (jarred or homemade), stemmed and seeded

2 tbsp fresh bread crumbs

1 egg yolk

1½ tsp salt

3 tbsp extra-virgin olive oil

1½ lb/680 g bulbing spring onions with their green tops (see Cook's Note)

Extra-virgin olive oil for brushing

Salt and freshly ground pepper

4 to 8 thick slices artisan bread

4 Crispy Fried Eggs (see page 61) or Crunchy Deep-Fried Eggs (see page 66)

PREPARATION

To make the romesco sauce: Slit the dried chile lengthwise and discard the stem and seeds. Tear it into little pieces and put in a small bowl with the tomatoes and vinegar to rehydrate for about 30 minutes. Put the hazelnuts and garlic in a food processor and pulse to finely mince. Add the tomato mixture, the roasted pepper, bread crumbs, egg yolk, and salt and process the mixture to a coarse purée, scraping down the sides of the bowl as needed. With the processor running, slowly drizzle in the olive oil through the feed tube. Taste and add more salt or vinegar as needed. The romesco could also, more authentically, be made with a mortar and pestle.

Prepare a hot fire in a charcoal grill or pre-heat a gas grill or stove-top grill pan to high. Trim and discard the very tips of the root ends and any wilted, dark green tops from the onions, leaving the crisp, lighter green parts still attached. Cut the onions in half lengthwise through the roots. Brush on both sides with oil to lightly coat (they shouldn't be dripping with oil), and sprinkle with a big pinch of salt and pepper.

Lightly oil the grill grates using a paper towel soaked in oil and a long pair of tongs. Arrange the onions on the grill perpendicular to the grates, with the cut-sides down and a little space between them (you may need to grill in two batches). Cook until charred evenly on the outside and tender inside, turning once, about 2 to 4 minutes per side, depending on the size of the onions. If the green tops become too dark, position them around the cooler parts of the grill so that the bulbs take the brunt of the heat. Transfer the grilled onions to a platter and loosely cover with aluminum foil to keep hot.

Brush the bread slices on both sides with a little oil, sprinkle with salt, and grill until each side is crunchy and charred with grill marks, 1 to 2 minutes.

Portion the onions onto four warmed plates. Spoon plenty of romesco sauce in a big dollop over the onions and top with an egg. Serve with the grilled bread on the side.

to drink: *Cava*

egg tip: *The eggs fry up so quickly that you should have everything else prepared first. Plate up the onions and sauce while they fry so that the landing pad is ready when the eggs are cooked.*

cook's note: *In the early spring, try to get your hands on* calçots, *Spanish spring onions with elongated bulbs and a mild, sweet flavor. Some American farms, like Viridian in Portland, Oregon, grow them for Spanish restaurants, and they may sell the surplus at the farmers' market. Any beautiful, bulby spring onions will work well here; you could even substitute ramps when available, or leeks at any time of the year.*

eggs on vegetables

STIR-FRIED BRUSSELS SPROUTS and WOK-FRIED EGGS

serves 2

INGREDIENTS

12 oz/340 g Brussels sprouts

Salt

2 tbsp Thai or Vietnamese fish sauce

1½ tsp fresh lime juice

1 tsp soy sauce

1 tsp sugar

2 tbsp peanut or vegetable oil

2 garlic cloves, thinly sliced

One 1-in/2.5-cm piece peeled fresh ginger, thinly sliced and cut into matchsticks

2 green onions, white and green parts, halved lengthwise and cut into 1½-in/4-cm segments

1 or 2 red Thai chiles, thinly sliced, or to taste

2 Wok-Fried Eggs (see page 64)

PREPARATION

Trim the Brussels sprouts and discard any brown or wilted outer leaves. Halve the smaller ones and quarter the larger ones. Keep any fresh-looking leaves that detach.

Fill a medium pot two-thirds full with water, add a few big pinches of salt, and bring to a boil over high heat. Add the Brussels sprouts and any loose leaves and cook until bright green and just beginning to tenderize, about 45 seconds. Drain well in a colander and cool under cold running water. Spread the Brussels sprouts and loose leaves out on a kitchen towel to dry and continue cooling.

Stir together the fish sauce, lime juice, soy sauce, and sugar in a small bowl and set it near the stove.

Before you get to stir-frying, know that this is a super-quick cooking process, so it is important to have all the ingredients prepped and ready to go into the wok on cue. I line the ingredients up next to the stove in the order that they will be added. Also, this is a high-heat cooking process, but if at any time the stir-fry begins to burn, reduce the heat briefly, add the next ingredient(s) to bring the temperature down, and then continue cooking over medium-high or high heat.

Heat a flat-bottomed wok over high heat. (This could be cooked in a 10-in/25-cm sauté pan over medium-high heat if you don't have a wok, but the timing will be a little different, so rely on the visual cues.) Add the oil and swirl to coat the bottom and edges of the pan. When you begin to see wisps of smoke, add the garlic and ginger and stir-fry until just brown at the edges, about 15 seconds. Quickly add the green onions and chiles and continue stir-frying until wilted, about 15 seconds more. Add the Brussels sprouts and stir-fry until lightly browned in some spots, 2 to 3 minutes. Pour in the fish sauce mixture and continue to stir-fry until the sauce is slightly thickened, about 1 minute more. Transfer the stir-fry to a warm platter.

Top with the eggs and serve family-style.

to drink: *Singha beer*

egg tip: *After plating the stir-fry, quickly wipe out the wok with paper towels and proceed with frying the eggs. The Brussels sprouts will stay hot in the short time it takes the eggs to cook.*

MISO-CReaMeD KaLe and MUSHROOMS WITH SOY Sauce eGGS

serves 2

INGREDIENTS

3 tbsp unsalted butter

1 large shallot, thinly sliced

2 garlic cloves, thinly sliced

Freshly ground pepper

1 bunch kale, preferably lacinato, thick center stems removed, leaves coarsely chopped

¼ cup/60 ml dry vermouth, sake, or white wine

½ cup/120 ml heavy (whipping) cream

¼ cup/70 g white miso paste

Salt

4 oz/115 g shimeji or shiitake mushrooms, cleaned and trimmed

1 tbsp soy sauce

2 cups/250 g cooked brown rice, hot

2 Japanese Soy Sauce Eggs (see page 33), warm or at room temperature

PREPARATION

Melt 2 tbsp of the butter in a large, heavy pot over medium heat. When it's bubbly, add the shallot, garlic, and a pinch of pepper. Sauté until tender and just beginning to brown, about 5 minutes. Add the kale, one big handful at a time, tossing with tongs to wilt the leaves in the hot fat before each addition. Cook the kale, stirring occasionally, until just tender and bright green, 3 to 5 minutes. Raise the heat to medium-high, add the vermouth, and cook until almost dry, about 1 minute. Stir in the cream and miso, reduce the heat to medium, and cook until it's a thick sauce that clings to the kale, about 5 minutes more. Taste and add salt and more pepper as needed, keeping in mind that the mushrooms and eggs will be quite salty because of the soy sauce.

Meanwhile, melt the remaining 1 tbsp of butter in a 10-in/25-cm sauté pan or skillet over medium-high heat. When it's bubbly, add the mushrooms and sauté until they've given up their liquid and then lightly browned, about 5 minutes. Stir in the soy sauce; it should be absorbed by the mushrooms and reduced to dry almost immediately.

Divide the rice between two warmed plates. Spoon a portion of the kale over each, and arrange the mushrooms on top and around the plates. Cut the eggs in half and nestle them on the side. Serve with chopsticks.

to drink: *chilled sake*

egg tip: *The eggs are best in this dish when they are cooked just before serving and still a little warm. They can be cooked several hours in advance, just be sure to remove them from the refrigerator to come to room temperature at least 1 hour before serving.*

cook's note: *This recipe was inspired by a dish created by chef Trent Pierce for his restaurant, Wafu, in Portland, Oregon.*

CHAPTER 5

EGGS
on GRAINS and
LEGUMES

TWENTY MINUTES TILL COUSCOUS 170

PIMENTO CHEESE GRITS WITH GREENS
AND MILK-POACHED EGGS 172

BAKED SWEET CORN POLENTA WITH
TOMATO SAUCE AND EGGS 174

FARROTTO WITH DELICATA SQUASH AND
SAGE-BROWN BUTTER EGGS 175

RISI E BISI 178

DUCK FRIED RICE WITH KUMQUATS
AND LOTS OF VEGGIES 179

AROMATIC LENTILS WITH SMOKED
TROUT AND DILLY EGGS 182

BASQUE PIPÉRADE BEANS WITH
BAKED EGGS 184

FULL ENGLISH BREAKFAST BOWL 185

twenty minutes till couscous

serves 4

INGREDIENTS

1 tbsp coriander seeds

1 tbsp cumin seeds

1¼ cup/300 ml water

Finely grated zest and juice of 1 large orange

Salt

1 cup/165 g couscous, preferably whole wheat

2 tbsp olive oil

3 cups/300 g bite-size cauliflower florets

1 large ripe tomato, diced, or 1 cup/255 g
   canned diced tomato

1 tsp harissa paste or ½ tsp red pepper flakes
   (see Cook's Note, page 131)

½ cup/90 g frozen peas

¼ cup/50 g coarsely chopped pitted oil-cured
   or kalamata olives

½ cup/10 g lightly packed coarsely chopped
   fresh cilantro

⅓ cup/75 ml plain Greek-style yogurt

4 Crispy Fried Eggs (see page 61)

¼ cup/10 g lightly packed coarsely chopped
   fresh mint (optional)

PREPARATION

Heat a small saucepan over medium heat. When it's hot, add the coriander and cumin and constantly swirl the pan until the seeds are aromatic and a shade darker, about 45 seconds. Add 1 cup/240 ml of the water, the orange zest and juice, and 1 tsp of salt and bring to a boil over high heat.

Put the couscous in a large bowl and rest a fine-mesh strainer over the top. When the liquid reaches a boil, pour it through the strainer into the bowl; discard the spices. Make sure the couscous is submerged, then cover tightly with plastic wrap and set aside until the liquid is completely absorbed, 7 to 10 minutes.

Meanwhile, heat the oil in a 10-in/25-cm sauté pan or skillet over medium-high heat. When you see wisps of smoke, add the cauliflower and a big pinch of salt. Spread the cauliflower out in the pan and cook without disturbing for about 2 minutes to deeply brown, then flip and continue cooking until the other side is deeply browned, about 2 minutes more. Add the tomato, harissa, and the remaining ¼ cup/60 ml water and cook until the cauliflower is tender throughout and the tomatoes reduce to a thick sauce, about 3 minutes. Stir in the peas and olives and cook about 1 minute more, until warmed through, then remove the pan from the heat.

Use a fork to comb the top layer of couscous, loosening it into fluffy granules. Continue combing layer by layer, until it's all freed and fluffy. Pour the cauliflower mixture into the bowl and toss it with the couscous. Gently mix in the cilantro (reserving some for garnish if you're not using mint).

Portion the couscous onto four warmed plates. Top with a dollop of yogurt, an egg, and mint (or the reserved cilantro) to serve.

to drink: *Moroccan mint tea*

egg tip: *Cook the eggs while you are tossing and seasoning the couscous.*

PIMENTO CHEESE GRITS WITH GREENS AND MILK-POACHED EGGS

serves 4

INGREDIENTS

Grits

2½ cups/600 ml milk

2½ cups/600 ml water

Salt

¾ cup/145 g stone-ground grits (white or yellow)

2 oz/55 g cream cheese, at room temperature

¾ cup/135 g diced fresh pimento or
    red bell peppers

Dash of hot sauce, or to taste

1 cup/85 g shredded extra-sharp Cheddar cheese

Freshly ground pepper

Greens

1 tbsp unsalted butter

3 garlic cloves, chopped

1 large bunch collard greens, stemmed
    and leaves torn into 2-in/5-cm pieces

¾ cup/180 ml homemade chicken or vegetable
    stock or store-bought low-sodium broth

Salt and freshly ground pepper

1 tsp finely grated lemon zest

1 tsp fresh lemon juice

4 Milk-Poached Eggs (see page 42),
    plus the poaching milk

Hot sauce for garnish

PREPARATION

To make the grits: Bring the milk, water, and a big pinch of salt to a boil in a medium, heavy pot over medium-high heat. Whisk in the grits and bring to a simmer. Reduce the heat to maintain a low simmer and cook, stirring occasionally, until the grits are as tender as you'd like, 45 minutes for coarser to 1½ hours for creamy. (If the grits become too dry, add more hot water as needed.) Stir in the cream cheese, pimento, and hot sauce and cook until the pimento is just tender, 6 to 8 minutes. Add the Cheddar and stir until melted. Taste and add more salt and pepper as needed.

To make the greens: Melt the butter in a large pot over medium heat. When it's bubbly, add the garlic and cook until soft and aromatic, about 2 minutes. Add the greens, stock, a big pinch of salt, a small pinch of pepper, and the zest and bring to a simmer, tossing the greens to wilt. Reduce the heat to medium-low, cover, and cook until tender, about 15 minutes. Stir in the lemon juice. Taste and add more salt and pepper as needed.

Portion the grits onto four warmed plates. Top with the greens and the eggs, with a little of the poaching milk. Garnish the eggs with salt and hot sauce and serve.

to drink: *Bloody Marys*

egg tip: *Cook the eggs just before serving, keeping the grits and greens covered and over low heat.*

BaKeD SWeeT CORN POLenTa WITH TOMaTO sauce anD eggs

serves 6

INGREDIENTS

2 cups/480 ml milk

2 cups/480 ml homemade chicken or vegetable stock, store-bought low-sodium broth, or water

1 cup/175 g polenta, coarse-ground cornmeal, or grits

1½ tsp salt

2 ears sweet corn, shucked

1 cup/115 g freshly grated Parmigiano-Reggiano cheese

Spicy Tomato Sauce with Onion and Butter (page 74), hot

6 room-temperature eggs

PREPARATION

Position a rack in the upper third of the oven and preheat it to 350°F/180°C/gas 4.

Stir together the milk, stock, polenta, and salt in a 2-qt/2-L shallow baking dish. Bake, uncovered, until the liquid is absorbed and the polenta is tender and bubbling, about 40 minutes, rotating the pan halfway through.

Meanwhile, cut the corn kernels off the cobs into a large bowl. Use the spine of the knife to scrape out any remaining corn juice from the cob into the bowl.

Stir the corn and its juice and about half the cheese into the polenta. Taste and add more salt as needed. Smooth the top, and continue baking until the surface dries and the polenta jiggles when you shake the pan, about 30 minutes more.

Remove the polenta to set for 10 to 20 minutes while you preheat the broiler.

Spread the tomato sauce over the top of the polenta. Make six shallow wells in the sauce only (don't dig into the polenta) and crack 1 egg into each. Sprinkle with the remaining cheese and broil until the egg whites are set, the yolks are still jiggly, and the cheese is melted and crusty, 3 to 5 minutes. Let the dish set for at least 5 minutes before serving.

For each serving, swoop up a big spoonful of polenta, sauce, and an egg onto warmed plates and serve.

to drink: *red or white wine from Friuli*

egg tip: *Be sure to broil the dish just until the whites are set but the yolks are still quite loose, because they will continue to cook out of the oven. Molten yolks provide a rich sauce for the polenta casserole.*

FARROTTO WITH DELICATA SQUASH AND SAGE–BROWN BUTTER EGGS

serves 4

INGREDIENTS

1 lb/455 g delicata squash, scrubbed

2 tbsp olive oil

Salt

Small pinch of piment d'Espelette or cayenne pepper

2 cups/480 ml water

4 cups/960 ml homemade chicken or vegetable stock or store-bought low-sodium broth

2 cups/380 g farro

2 tbsp unsalted butter

½ yellow onion, diced

2 large garlic cloves, minced

½ cup/120 ml dry white wine

¼ cup/30 g freshly grated Parmigiano-Reggiano cheese

4 Sage–Brown Butter Eggs (see page 62), plus the browned butter and fried sage

PREPARATION

Preheat the oven to 450°F/230°C/gas 8.

Halve the squash lengthwise and scoop out and discard the seeds. Cut the unpeeled squash into ½-in/12-mm pieces. Toss with 1 tbsp of the oil, a big pinch of salt, and piment d'Espelette in a large bowl. Spread the squash out on a rimmed baking sheet and roast until the flesh is tender and browned around the edges, stirring once or twice, 15 to 20 minutes. The squash can be refrigerated for up to 2 days.

Bring the water, 2 cups/480 ml of the stock, the farro, and a few big pinches of salt to a boil in a medium pot over high heat. Reduce the heat to maintain a steady simmer, and cook, stirring occasionally, until most of the liquid has been absorbed and the farro is tender but still quite chewy, about 30 minutes. Drain well, collecting the cooking liquid in a small saucepan. Set the farro aside.

Add the remaining 2 cups/480 ml of stock to the saucepan with the cooking liquid. Bring it to a simmer over high heat, then reduce the heat to low to keep it hot while you're making the farrotto. Have ready a 1-cup/240-ml ladle or a measuring cup with a handle.

Heat the remaining 1 tbsp oil with the butter in a 12-in/30.5-cm skillet over medium heat. When the butter is bubbly, add the onion and garlic and sauté until the onion is translucent and starting to brown, 8 to 10 minutes. Add the farro and cook, stirring constantly, for about 1 minute. Add the wine, raise the heat to medium-high, and simmer until almost dry.

Next you're going to add the hot stock to the farro mixture in three 1-cup/240-ml increments, allowing the farro to absorb most of the stock before each addition. Stir the mixture occasionally after adding the stock, while it's still very fluid, and then begin to stir it almost constantly when it's about half absorbed. Adjust the heat up or down to maintain a simmer with steady bubbles. Cook the

continued

final addition of stock down to the point that it is almost completely absorbed but not dry; the farrotto should appear moist and just a little saucy at the bottom of the pot. You're looking for the farro to be relatively tender yet retain its characteristic chewy texture. This process of adding liquid and cooking it down will take a total of 20 to 25 minutes. (For a dinner party, you could make the farrotto up to this point, and then cover and refrigerate it for up to 1 day. Reheat over medium heat on the stove top and finish to serve.)

Reduce the heat to low and stir in the cheese and roasted squash. Taste and add more salt as needed. Keep the farrotto over low heat until the squash is warmed through and you are ready to plate it with the eggs. Stir in a little water if it becomes too dry.

Portion the farrotto into four warmed bowls and top each with an egg. Pour some of the brown butter over the top and garnish with the fried sage to serve.

to drink: *Dolcetto d'Alba*

egg tip: *Wait to cook the eggs until the farrotto is finished and being held over low heat.*

RISI e BISI

serves 4

INGREDIENTS

4 cups/960 ml homemade chicken or vegetable stock or store-bought low-sodium broth

Salt

6 oz/170 g sugar snap peas

½ tbsp unsalted butter

2 oz/55 g pancetta, diced

½ cup/100 g diced yellow onion

1 cup/215 g Arborio or Carnaroli rice

¼ cup/60 ml dry white wine

⅓ cup/40 g freshly grated Parmigiano-Reggiano cheese

2 oz/55 g pea shoots, tender leaves and tendrils only

4 Quintessential Poached Eggs (see page 38) or Foolproof Poached Eggs (see page 44)

Freshly ground pepper

PREPARATION

Bring the stock and a large pinch of salt to a boil in a medium pot over high heat. Trim the stems from the snap peas and pull off the fibrous strings that run along the seams. Slice the pods in half lengthwise, on a diagonal, to expose the peas inside. Drop the pea pods and any renegade peas into the stock and cook just long enough to take away the raw crispness, about 1 minute. Strain the peas using a slotted spoon or a spider and set in a bowl. Reduce the heat to low and cover the pot to keep the stock hot.

Meanwhile, melt the butter in a heavy soup pot over medium heat. When it's bubbly, add the pancetta and sauté until crisp and browned at the edges but still a little chewy, about 5 minutes. Add the onion and cook, stirring occasionally with a wooden spoon, until tender and golden, 5 to 7 minutes.

Add the rice and stir to coat with a nice sheen of fat, about 30 seconds, then add the wine and stir constantly until it's almost completely absorbed, taking care to get the bottom and edges of the pot, 1 to 2 minutes. Pour in about 3½ cups/840 ml of the hot stock, raise the heat to medium-high, and bring to a simmer. (Keep the remaining stock nearby to thin the porridge later.) Reduce the heat to maintain a low, steady simmer; the goal is to allow the rice to absorb the liquid without evaporating too quickly. Cook, stirring the bottom and edges of the pot quite often, until the rice is tender but still just a little too chewy in the center, about 18 minutes.

Stir in the cheese, snap peas, and about two-thirds of the pea shoots. Add more of the broth to thin the dish to the point that it must be eaten with a spoon, as it should be. Water can be added, too, if needed. Taste and add more salt as needed. When the peas are bright green and crisp-tender and the rice is chewy and swimming in a creamy sauce, spoon the porridge into four warmed bowls and place a bushy bouquet of the remaining pea shoots in the center of each. Nestle in the eggs and garnish with a sprinkle of pepper.

to drink: *Prosecco*

egg tip: *Cook the eggs just before adding the cheese and peas. They will be done at about the same time.*

DUCK FRIED RICE WITH KUMQUATS AND LOTS OF VEGGIES

serves 2

INGREDIENTS

4 kumquats, thinly sliced and seeded

1 tsp sugar

2 tbsp soy sauce

1 tbsp Shaoxing wine (see Cook's Note, page 77), dry sherry, or water

¼ tsp salt

Pinch of freshly ground white pepper

2 tbsp duck fat, or peanut or vegetable oil (see Cook's Notes)

3 garlic cloves, minced

1 tbsp minced peeled fresh ginger

1 large shallot, thinly sliced

1 medium carrot, peeled and thinly sliced on a diagonal

1 celery stalk, thinly sliced

1 cup/135 g Chinese roasted duck meat and skin, shredded and chopped into bite-size pieces (see Cook's Notes)

2 cups/250 g cooked brown or white rice, preferably day-old, at room temperature

2 cups/110 g finely shredded napa or savoy cabbage

3 green onions, white and green parts, thinly sliced

3 tbsp coarsely chopped fresh cilantro, plus a handful of leaves for garnish

2 Wok-Fried Eggs (see page 64), preferably duck eggs fried in duck fat

PREPARATION

Toss the kumquats in the sugar in a small bowl and set aside for 20 to 30 minutes. Stir together the soy sauce, wine, salt, and pepper in another small bowl and set it near the stove.

Before you get to stir-frying, know that this is a super-quick cooking process, so it is important to have all the ingredients prepped and ready to go into the wok on cue. I line the ingredients up next to the stove in the order that they will be added. Also, this is a high-heat cooking process, but if at any time the stir-fry begins to burn, reduce the heat briefly, add the next ingredient(s) to bring the temperature down, and then continue cooking over medium-high or high heat.

Heat a flat-bottomed wok over high heat. (This could be cooked in a large sauté pan or a Dutch oven over medium-high heat if you don't own a wok, but the timing will be different, so rely on the visual cues.) Add the duck fat and swirl to coat the bottom and edges of the pan. When you begin to see wisps of smoke, add the garlic and ginger and stir-fry until just brown at the edges, about 15 seconds. Quickly add the shallot and stir-fry until slightly softened, about 30 seconds. Add the carrot and celery and stir-fry until slightly softened, about 3 minutes. Add the duck meat and kumquats and cook until heated through and the carrots and celery are tender but still firm, about 1 minute. Add the rice, cabbage,

continued

and half of the green onions and stir-fry to lightly toast the rice, scraping the bottom of the pan if it sticks, about 1 minute. Pour in the soy sauce mixture and continue to stir-fry, tossing and flipping the ingredients together, until the sauce is evenly distributed and absorbed, about 1 minute. Stir in the chopped cilantro. Transfer the fried rice to a warmed platter. Put the eggs on top and sprinkle with a handful of cilantro leaves and the remaining green onions and serve family-style.

to drink: *Pinot Noir*

egg tip: *When the fried rice is done, loosely cover with aluminum foil to stay hot while you cook the eggs. Wash and dry the wok, then cook the eggs. They cook so quickly that the rice will stay hot, but the flavor is best when it has cooled for a few minutes anyway. To eat, I like to cut up the eggs right away and swirl the yolk around to moisten the rice.*

cook's notes: *Duck fat can be purchased at good butcher shops and specialty grocery stores.*

Roasted duck is available from many Chinese restaurants and Asian markets. Some grocery stores also stock fresh or frozen cooked duck meat, which would work, too. When I order Chinese take-out in the wintertime, when kumquats are in season, I get extra duck and rice with the intent of making this dish the following day.

EGGS ON GRAINS AND LEGUMES

aromatic Lentils with smoked trout and Dilly eggs

serves 2

INGREDIENTS

½ cup/125 g beluga lentils

1 small yellow onion, halved

1 celery stalk, halved

1 carrot, halved

2 garlic cloves, smashed

1 bay leaf

1 bunch baby turnips or radishes

2 tbsp extra-virgin olive oil, plus more for drizzling

Salt and freshly ground pepper

1 tsp sherry vinegar, plus more as needed

1 tsp Dijon mustard

¼ cup/60 ml crème fraîche or sour cream

3 oz/85 g smoked trout or salmon, shredded into large bite-size pieces

2 tbsp coarsely chopped fresh dill fronds

4 Foolproof Poached Eggs (see page 44), made with fresh dill sprigs

PREPARATION

Put the lentils, onion, celery, carrot, garlic, and bay leaf in a medium pot and fill it with enough cold water to cover them by at least 1 in/2.5 cm. Bring to a boil over high heat, then reduce the heat to maintain a low simmer until the lentils are tender but just a little underdone, about 15 minutes. Drain the lentils in a colander, reserving 1 cup/240 ml of the cooking liquid. Rinse the lentils under cold running water to cool. Spread them out on a kitchen towel to continue cooling and drying. Pick out and discard the onion, celery, carrot, garlic, and bay leaf.

Trim the turnip tops, leaving 1 in/2.5 cm of the stems intact. Halve them lengthwise, bisecting the stems, so that each half has a little of the stem still attached.

Heat the oil in a 10-in/25-cm sauté pan or skillet over medium-high heat. When it's shimmering hot, add the turnips, cut-sides down, and cook until evenly browned and tender, about 5 minutes, swirling the pan and moving them about to cook evenly, but never turning them over. Reduce the heat to medium and add the lentils, just enough of the reserved cooking liquid to moisten (about ¼ cup/60 ml), ½ tsp salt, and a pinch of pepper. Bring to a simmer, stirring occasionally. Stir in the vinegar and mustard.

Turn off the heat and stir in the crème fraîche, then the trout and dill, tossing gently to avoid breaking up the trout. Taste and add more salt, pepper, or vinegar as needed.

Divide the lentils between two warm bowls. Top each bowl with 2 eggs, drizzle with a little olive oil, and serve.

to drink: *chilled aquavit or white wine from the Loire Valley*

egg tip: *Poach the eggs, and then cool them in an ice bath, keeping them in the plastic wrap. Just before serving, drop them back into a pot of slowly simmering water to rewarm, then unwrap.*

BasQue PipéRade Beans
WiTH BaKeD eGGs

serves 6

INGREDIENTS

2 cups/380 g dried cannellini or great Northern
    beans, picked over

3 tbsp olive oil

3 bell peppers in a variety of colors, seeded,
    deribbed, and thinly sliced

1 small yellow onion, thinly sliced

6 garlic cloves, smashed

3 large tomatoes, cored and coarsely chopped,
    or one 14.5-oz/415-g can diced tomatoes

2 tsp piment d'Espelette or hot paprika

2 cups/480 ml homemade chicken, pork,
    or vegetable stock, or water (see Cook's Note)

1 meaty smoked ham hock

Salt

¼ cup/10 g chopped fresh parsley

6 room-temperature eggs

PREPARATION

Soak the beans in 6 cups/1.4 L water for at
least 6 hours, preferably overnight.

Heat the oil in a 12-in/30.5-cm heavy skillet
over medium-high heat. When it's shimmering, add the bell peppers, onion, and garlic.
Cook, stirring often, until lightly browned and
softened, 7 to 9 minutes. Add the tomatoes
and cook down until they're a thick sauce, 8 to
10 minutes. Stir in the piment d'Espelette.

Drain and rinse the beans and put them in a
Dutch oven with the pipérade, stock, and ham
hock and bring to a boil over medium-high

heat. Reduce the heat to maintain a low simmer and cook, stirring occasionally, until the
beans are tender, 2 to 2½ hours. Cover the pot
after about 1 hour, when the liquid thickens.
Add a little water to the pot, if needed, to keep
the beans just barely covered. Add a few big
pinches of salt when the beans are noticeably
softened, about halfway through cooking.

Preheat the oven to 400°F/200°C/gas 6 at
least 20 minutes before the beans are done.

Pull the meat from the ham hock in bite-
size shreds and stir it back into the beans;
discard the excess fat and the bone. Stir in
the parsley, then taste and add more salt
as needed.

Divide the beans between six shallow
baking dishes, each about 1 in/2.5 cm high and
7 in/17 cm wide. Make a well in the center of
each and crack in 1 egg. (Alternatively, the
beans and eggs can be baked in one 12-in/
30.5-cm skillet.) Bake until the eggs are cooked
to your liking, 10 to 15 minutes. Let cool 5 minutes before serving.

to drink: *Rioja*

egg tip: *Pull the beans from the oven when the egg
whites are opaque but still a little jiggly in the
center; the eggs will finish out of the oven.*

cook's note: *Don't use store-bought broth that contains sodium; it makes the beans tough.*

FULL ENGLISH BREAKFAST BOWL

serves 4

INGREDIENTS

8 oz/225 g thick-cut bacon, cut into ½-in/
  12-mm strips

10 oz/280 g cremini mushrooms, halved

1 tsp chopped fresh thyme

Salt and freshly ground pepper

Two 13.7-oz/390-g cans Heinz Beans with
  Tomato Sauce (see Cook's Note)

4 ripe plum tomatoes

1½ tsp extra-virgin olive oil

1 tbsp finely chopped fresh parsley

4 Panfried Eggs (see page 56), fried in bacon fat

4 slices buttered toast

PREPARATION

Heat a 10-in/25-cm skillet over medium-high
heat. Add the bacon and sauté until crispy on
the edges but still fatty, about 5 minutes. Use
a slotted spoon to transfer the bacon to a plate
lined with a paper towel. Pour off all but about
2 tbsp of fat, reserving the excess fat to fry the
eggs. Add the mushrooms and sauté until
they've given up their liquid and then
browned, about 5 minutes. Stir in the thyme
and a pinch of salt and pepper when they just
begin to brown. Transfer the cooked mushrooms to a bowl and cover.

Reduce the heat to medium-low and add the
beans to the pan. Stir in the bacon and a pinch
of pepper and bring to a simmer. Cook until
the beans are hot and the liquid thickens
slightly, about 5 minutes. Taste and add more
salt and pepper as needed.

Meanwhile, heat a grill pan or cast-iron skillet over medium-high heat. Core and cut the
tomatoes in half lengthwise. Scoop out and
discard the seeds. Toss the tomatoes in a large
bowl with the oil and a pinch of salt. Arrange
the tomatoes, cut-side down, in the grill pan
and cook, without moving, until deeply
charred grill marks appear, or until they are
evenly browned, if cooking in a skillet, 2 to
3 minutes. Flip the tomatoes, reduce the heat
to medium, and cook until the skins are lightly
charred and the tomatoes are tender throughout but not mushy, 3 to 4 minutes more. Return
the grilled tomatoes to the bowl as they are
done and gently toss with parsley.

Spoon a portion of the beans in the center
of each of four warm, shallow bowls. Spoon a
portion of the mushrooms in each bowl, along
one edge, partially covering the beans. Nestle
a few tomatoes along the opposite edge of the
beans. Place 1 egg in the center and serve with
toast on the side.

to drink: *a Black and Tan*

egg tip: *Fry the eggs when the other components of
the dish are all cooked and ready to be plated.*

cook's note: *Heinz-brand baked beans are different from most American-style canned baked beans
because the sauce has more tomato flavor and is
less sweet. I buy them at Cost Plus World Market,
but you may find them at other specialty food stores,
or on Amazon.*

CHAPTER **6**

EGGS on NOODLES

nests of carbonara 188

whole-wheat spaghetti, tuna,
chiles, eggs, and pangrattato 191

shells and cheese with caramelized
fennel and crispy breaded eggs 192

shrimp pad thai 194

kimchi ramen 197

garlic-scallion noodles 199

soba noodle salad with soft
eggs, kale, and kabocha 200

nests of carbonara

serves 4

INGREDIENTS

Salt

12 oz/340 g long pasta, such as spaghetti, linguine, or bucatini

1 tbsp extra-virgin olive oil

6 oz/170 g bacon, cut into lardons (see Cook's Note, page 148)

⅓ cup/75 ml white wine

2 eggs plus 4 egg yolks

½ cup/60 g freshly grated Parmigiano-Reggiano, plus more for garnish

½ cup/60 g freshly grated Pecorino Romano

¼ cup/10 g finely chopped fresh parsley

½ tsp freshly ground black pepper

½ tsp freshly ground pink pepper, plus more for garnish (optional)

½ cup/90 g shelled fresh English peas or thawed frozen peas

PREPARATION

Bring a large pot of well-salted water to a boil over high heat. Drop in the pasta, stir, and cook to al dente according to the package instructions.

Meanwhile, heat the oil in a 10-in/25-cm skillet over medium-high heat. When it's shimmering hot, add the bacon and sauté until crispy on the edges but still fatty and meaty in the center, 3 to 5 minutes. Add the wine (watch for splatter!) and cook until almost dry, about 2 minutes. Remove the pan from the heat to cool slightly.

Whisk together the whole eggs, the cheeses, parsley, and black and pink pepper in a large bowl. Slowly whisk in the warm bacon and all the fat from the pan, gently cooking the eggs without scrambling them.

About 1 minute before the pasta is done, stir the peas into the pot. Take out ¼ cup/60 ml of the cooking water and slowly whisk it into the bowl of eggs and bacon to thin the sauce.

Drain the pasta and peas and immediately add them to the sauce, tossing to coat the piping-hot noodles well. Using tongs, coil the pasta into four warmed shallow bowls. Place an egg yolk in the center of each coil (in half an eggshell, as pictured, if desired). Dust with lots of Parmigiano-Reggiano and pink pepper, if desired, and serve.

to drink: *Chianti Classico*

egg tip: *Separate the yolks in advance, and leave them to rest at room temperature in half their shell while you prepare the dish. Encourage your guests to swirl the raw yolk into the pasta to complete the sauce.*

WHOLE-WHEAT SPAGHETTI, TUNA, CHILES, EGGS, AND PANGRATTATO

serves 4

INGREDIENTS

2 tsp extra-virgin olive oil plus 2 tbsp

3 tbsp coarse fresh bread crumbs

1 tbsp finely chopped fresh parsley

Salt

10 oz/280 g whole-wheat spaghetti

½ cup/40 g coarsely chopped sun-dried tomatoes, drained if packed in oil

One 6.7-oz/190-g jar tuna packed in olive oil (see Cook's Note)

3 cups/75 g lightly packed baby arugula or spinach

4 Garlic-Chile Eggs (see page 62)

PREPARATION

Heat the 2 tsp oil in a small skillet over medium-high heat. Add the bread crumbs and sauté until crisp, golden brown, and moist like sand. Stir in the parsley and a pinch of salt. Transfer the bread crumbs to a small bowl.

Bring a large pot of well-salted water to a boil over high heat. Drop in the pasta, stir, and cook to al dente according to the package instructions.

Meanwhile, if the sun-dried tomatoes weren't packed in oil, put them in a small dish and ladle in enough of the boiling pasta water to cover. Soak them for about 5 minutes to reconstitute, then drain.

A few minutes before the pasta is finished cooking, warm the remaining 2 tbsp of oil over medium-low heat in a large pot. Stir in the tuna and sun-dried tomatoes and heat just to warm through.

When the pasta is done, drain, reserving about ½ cup/120 ml of the cooking water. Add the pasta, arugula, and a pinch of salt to the tuna mixture and toss to combine over medium-low heat. Add a little of the pasta water, just enough to moisten. Taste and add more salt as needed. Remove from the heat and cover to keep the pasta hot until you're ready to serve.

Divide the pasta among four warm bowls. Top each with an egg and a dusting of the seasoned bread crumbs before serving.

to drink: *Verdicchio*

egg tip: *Fry the eggs when the pasta is tossed and ready to serve, since they cook quickly.*

cook's note: *Don't skimp on the tuna here. Look for high-quality, imported tuna packed in olive oil. If you find ventresca (tuna belly), that will be even better. The size of the jars sold in stores can vary, but any amount between 6 and 8 oz/170 and 225 g will work just fine in this recipe.*

SHELLS AND CHEESE WITH CARAMELIZED FENNEL AND CRISPY BREADED EGGS

serves 4

INGREDIENTS

1 large fennel bulb

2 tbsp unsalted butter

Salt

¼ cup/60 ml dry white wine

1½ cups/360 ml heavy (whipping) cream

Freshly ground pepper

8 oz/225 g aged Cheddar cheese, shredded (or any blend of good melting cheeses), at room temperature

¼ cup/30 g freshly grated Parmigiano-Reggiano cheese

10 oz/280 g bite-size pasta shells, preferably whole wheat

4 Breaded Eggs (see page 67)

PREPARATION

Trim the green stalks and any brown spots from the fennel bulb and discard. Reserve some of the fronds for garnish. Cut the bulb in half lengthwise and cut out the core, then thinly slice into ¼-in/6-mm strips.

Melt the butter over medium heat in a medium, heavy pot, such as a Dutch oven. When it's bubbly, add the fennel and ½ tsp salt. Sauté until the fennel is very tender and evenly golden brown, 20 to 25 minutes. Reduce the heat to medium-low in the last 5 to 10 minutes of cooking if it begins to brown too quickly or too darkly.

Pour in the wine and cook until dry, about 1 minute. Add the cream and a pinch of pepper and bring to a boil over medium-high heat. Reduce the heat to medium and simmer, stirring often, until it reduces by about half, 8 to 10 minutes. Reduce the heat to low and add the Cheddar cheese in two big handfuls, stirring until each addition is fully melted before adding the next. Add the Parmigiano-Reggiano and stir until melted. Continue to cook a few minutes, stirring constantly over gentle heat, until the sauce is velvety and quite thick (it will be thinned by the pasta water). Taste and add more salt and pepper as needed.

Meanwhile, bring a large pot of well-salted water to a boil over high heat. Drop in the pasta, stir, and cook to al dente according to the package instructions. Shells tend to stick to the bottom of the pot, so be sure to stir every few minutes or so. Drain, reserving about ½ cup/120 ml of the cooking water.

Stir the hot shells into the cheese sauce and add enough of the pasta water to thin to a nice saucy consistency. Cook over gentle heat for a few minutes, stirring occasionally, to allow the sauce to saturate the noodles. Add more pasta water as needed, keeping in mind that the sauce will continue thickening once it is off the heat and in the bowls, so it should be a little loose in the pot.

Portion the shells and cheese into warm small bowls and top each with an egg laid on its side. Just before serving, cut a slit in each egg to let the yolk flow. Garnish with a tuft of fennel fronds crowning the eggs and serve immediately.

to drink: *dry Alsatian Riesling*

egg tip: *The eggs should be cooked in advance and then fried after the pasta is stirred into the sauce, just before serving. If you prefer to focus on one thing at a time, you can cover the finished pot of shells and cheese and place it in a warm oven to stay hot while you do the frying.*

SHRIMP PAD THAI

serves 2

INGREDIENTS

1½ tbsp seedless tamarind pulp (see Cook's Notes)

1 tbsp finely chopped palm sugar or light brown sugar (see Cook's Note, page 142)

1 tbsp preserved radish (optional; see Cook's Notes)

5 oz/140 g semidried or fully dried thin flat rice noodles (see Cook's Notes)

1½ tbsp Thai fish sauce, plus more for serving

1 to 2 tsp Sriracha sauce, plus more for serving

2 tbsp lard or peanut or vegetable oil

2 room-temperature eggs

One 2-in/5-cm piece pressed tofu, cut into ½-in/12-mm cubes (see Cook's Notes)

1 tbsp medium dried shrimp, rinsed and patted dry (see Cook's Notes)

6 medium fresh shrimp, peeled, deveined, and halved lengthwise

1 cup/80 g bean sprouts

4 garlic chives, cut into 1½-in/4-cm segments, or 2 green onions, white and green parts, halved lengthwise and cut into 1½-in/4-cm segments

¼ cup/40 g chopped roasted unsalted peanuts

2 lime wedges

Granulated sugar for garnish

PREPARATION

Bring ½ cup/120 ml of water to a boil in a small saucepan. Remove it from the heat and add the tamarind pulp and palm sugar. Break up the pulp with a wooden spoon, then cover and set aside to soften, about 10 minutes. Put the preserved radish, if using, in a small bowl, add enough hot tap water to completely submerge, and soak 10 minutes, then drain well. Put the noodles into a large bowl, add enough hot tap water to completely submerge, and soak until pliable but not soft, 8 to 10 minutes. Drain the noodles, rinse under cold running water, and drain again very well.

Mash up the softened tamarind pulp to dissolve. There will likely be seeds and fibrous skins, so pour the mixture through a fine-mesh sieve into a small bowl and use the back of the wooden spoon to aggressively mash and push as much of the pulp through as possible; discard the solids. Stir the fish sauce and Sriracha into the tamarind water.

Before you get to stir-frying, know that this is a super-quick cooking process, so it is important to have all the ingredients prepped and ready to go into the wok on cue. I line the ingredients up next to the stove in the order that they will be added. Also, this is a high-heat cooking process, but if at any time the stir-fry begins to burn, reduce the heat briefly, add the next ingredient(s) to bring the temperature down, and then continue cooking over medium-high or high heat.

Heat a seasoned carbon-steel or nonstick wok over high heat. Add the lard and swirl to coat the bottom and edges of the wok. When you begin to see wisps of smoke, add the eggs; they will spit and splatter enthusiastically. After about 45 seconds, the eggs will be crispy and browned on the bottom. Turn the eggs, flipping away from you to avoid splatter, and quickly chop them into several pieces with the spatula. Push the eggs up the side of the wok or transfer to a plate.

Reduce the heat to medium-high and add the tofu, dried shrimp, and salted radish, if using. Stir-fry, avoiding the eggs, until the tofu and shrimp are lightly toasted, about 30 seconds. Add the fresh shrimp, stir the egg back in, and continue stir-frying until the fresh shrimp are pink but still a little undercooked inside, 1 to 2 minutes. Add the noodles and sprouts and toss to mix everything together. Pour in the tamarind mixture and stir-fry, tossing and flipping the noodles, until the mixture is evenly distributed and absorbed, about 2 minutes. Stir in the chives and half of the peanuts and remove the wok from the heat.

Divide the pad thai between two plates. Sprinkle with the remaining peanuts and serve with lime wedges, granulated sugar, and more fish sauce and Sriracha at the table.

to drink: *Singha beer*

egg tip: *The goal with the eggs in this dish is to first brown the whites on one side, and then to coarsely chop the eggs after flipping, while the yolks are still runny. The yolks will eventually be cooked through as the eggs are stir-fried with the other ingredients.*

cook's notes: *I discovered this authentic method of making pad thai when I tested the recipes for Andy Ricker's* Pok Pok *cookbook. This recipe is inspired by his, with a little extra egg, of course, and a few shortcuts to streamline the preparation at home.*

There are several ingredients in this recipe that can be found at Asian markets, especially those that specialize in Southeast Asian cuisines.

Tamarind pulp provides the sweet and sour flavor in pad thai (not ketchup!). Look for seedless tamarind pulp removed from the pod and compressed into a sticky, dense block, rather than tamarind concentrate, which has an inferior flavor.

Preserved radish has a salty funkiness that adds authentic flavor to the dish, but it may be a little more difficult to find. Look for the beige shredded radish packed in a plastic bag in the preserved vegetable aisle at most Asian markets.

The thin, flat rice noodles used in pad thai will be labeled rice sticks, pad thai, or banh pho, and come in two forms: semi-dried or fully dried. The semi-dried are better for this dish and can be found refrigerated in Asian markets, but the fully dried version is easier to find because it is typically sold in the international aisle at many supermarkets. The two forms can be treated and used interchangeably in this recipe.

Pressed tofu is, just as it sounds, tofu that has been pressed to extract most of the moisture, so it is more dense and dry than other forms and crisps up better in stir-fries. Extra-firm tofu can be substituted in a pinch by cutting it into ½-in/12-mm slabs and pressing it between a kitchen towel (not terry cloth) until most of the moisture is extracted.

Dried shrimp come in various sizes, but medium work best in this recipe. Look for them in a plastic bag that's labeled with an M (for medium) in the refrigerated section of most Asian markets.

KIMCHI RAMEN

serves 4

INGREDIENTS

6 cups/1.4 L homemade chicken or pork stock or store-bought low-sodium broth

14 oz/400 g skinless pork belly, cut against the grain into 8 slices that are ½ in/12 mm thick and 5 in/12 cm long

6 quarter-size slices unpeeled fresh ginger

6 garlic cloves, smashed

3 tbsp soy sauce

Salt

2 tbsp hoisin sauce

2 tsp sugar

2 cups/370 g drained kimchi, cut into bite-size pieces

12 oz/340 g dried or 18 oz/510 g fresh ramen noodles

4 Japanese Soy Sauce Eggs (page 33) or Coddled Eggs (page 31)

2 green onions, white and green parts, thinly sliced on a diagonal

PREPARATION

Put the stock, pork belly, ginger, garlic, 2 tbsp of the soy sauce, and 1 tsp salt in a medium saucepan and bring to a boil over high heat. Reduce the heat to maintain a low simmer, cover, and cook until the pork is tender but still a little chewy, 35 to 40 minutes.

Position an oven rack about 4 in/10 cm from the top heating element and preheat the broiler. Stir together the remaining 1 tbsp of soy sauce with the hoisin sauce and sugar in a medium bowl; set aside.

Remove the pork belly from the broth with a slotted spoon and pat it dry with paper towels. Strain the broth through a fine-mesh strainer into a large bowl, then pour it back into the pan; discard the solids. Toss the pork in the hoisin sauce mixture to lightly coat and arrange the strips on a rimmed baking sheet lined with aluminum foil. Add a ladleful of broth to the bowl to thin the remaining hoisin sauce clinging to the sides and pour it back into the pot to season the broth. Broil the meat until a charred crust forms on both sides, turning once, 3 to 5 minutes per side. Transfer the pork to a plate and cover to keep warm; save the rendered fat for another use (such as frying eggs!).

continued

Stir the kimchi into the broth and bring to a simmer over medium heat. Taste and add more salt as needed. Cover and keep the broth hot over low heat.

Meanwhile, bring at least 2 qt/2 L of water to a boil in a large pot over high heat. Add the noodles and cook, stirring occasionally, until tender but chewy, 2 to 3 minutes. Drain the noodles and portion them into four large, deep bowls. Drape 2 slices of pork belly over one side of the noodles in each bowl. Use a slotted spoon to remove the kimchi from the broth and place it in the bowls, next to the pork. Ladle in the broth, dividing it evenly. If you're using Soy Sauce Eggs, cut them in half and place two halves in each bowl. For Coddled Eggs, crack the shells and slip the eggs directly into the broth. Drop a heap of green onions in the center of each bowl and serve, with chopsticks and Asian-style soup spoons, if you have them.

to drink: *sake or Sapporo beer*

egg tip: *Prepare the eggs while the pork belly is cooking in the broth, and then cool until the dish is ready to be served. The eggs will reheat quickly in the hot broth.*

garLic-scaLLion noodLes

serves 2

INGREDIENTS

Peanut or vegetable oil for frying

4 scallions or green onions, white and light green
parts, cut into 2-in/5-cm julienne, green tops
thinly sliced on a diagonal

Salt

8 oz/225 g fresh thin Chinese egg noodles
(usually labeled wonton noodles)
or 6 oz/170 g dried angel hair pasta

5 garlic cloves, minced

¼ cup/60 ml chicken or vegetable stock or
store-bought low-sodium broth

2 tbsp soy sauce, or to taste

1 tsp sherry vinegar, or to taste

1 tsp light brown sugar

2 Sunny-Side Up Eggs (see page 56) or Chinese
Tea Eggs (page 34), quartered

PREPARATION

Fill a small, heavy saucepan with about ½ in/
12 mm of oil and heat it over medium heat
until a deep-frying thermometer registers
325°F/165°C. Or to test if the oil is hot enough
for frying, drop in a piece of scallion and see if
it bubbles vigorously right away. Add the julienned scallions and immediately reduce the
heat to low. Fry until most are light golden
brown, stirring occasionally, about 1½ minutes. (They will continue to darken and crisp
as they cool.) Have ready a small fine-mesh
strainer set over a heat-proof bowl. Pour the

scallions and oil into the strainer. Shake the
scallions from the excess oil and transfer to a
plate lined with a paper towel. Reserve the oil.

Bring a large pot of well-salted water to a
boil over high heat. Drop in the noodles, stir,
and cook according to the package instructions until tender but chewy, about 2 minutes.
Drain and rinse under cold running water to
cool, then drain again and set aside.

Heat 2 tbsp of the scallion oil in a flat-
bottomed wok or Dutch oven over medium
heat. When it's shimmering hot, add the garlic
and fry until soft and aromatic but not brown,
about 2 minutes. Pour in the stock, soy sauce,
vinegar, and sugar. Raise the heat to medium-
high and bring to a boil. Boil the sauce until
it's reduced by about a third and slightly
thickened, about 2 minutes. Stir in the noodles
and sliced scallion tops, tossing to coat well.
Cook for 1 to 2 minutes, until the noodles
absorb most of the sauce. Taste and add soy
sauce, vinegar, or salt as needed.

Divide the noodles between two warm
bowls. Top each bowl with an egg and a stack
of fried scallions and serve.

to drink: *Tsingtao beer*

egg tip: *For Sunny-Side Up Eggs, start cooking
them in the reserved scallion oil when the noodles
are added to the wok. They should be done at about
the same time. If you're using Chinese Tea Eggs,
they should be done before beginning this recipe.*

soBa noodLe saLaD WITH SOFT eGGs, kaLe, anD kaBoCHa

serves 4

INGREDIENTS

3 tsp Asian sesame oil

4 tsp honey

Salt

3 cups/360 g bite-size pieces of peeled kabocha
squash or other winter squash

8 oz/225 g soba noodles

2½ tbsp tahini

2 tbsp rice vinegar

1½ tbsp soy sauce

1 tbsp grated peeled fresh ginger

3 cups/60 g lightly packed kale leaves,
preferably purple, torn into bite-size pieces

Four 5-Minute Eggs (see page 28), at
room temperature

2 green onions, white and green parts, thinly
sliced on a severe diagonal

Togarashi (or other chile pepper) for garnish

PREPARATION

Preheat the oven to 450°F/230°C/gas 8.

Whisk together 2 tsp of the sesame oil, 2 tsp
of the honey, and ½ tsp salt in a large bowl and
add the squash, tossing to coat well. Spread
the squash out on a rimmed baking sheet
and roast until tender and deeply browned on
the bottoms and edges, 10 to 15 minutes. Set
aside to cool to room temperature.

Bring a large pot of well-salted water to a boil
over high heat. Drop in the noodles, stir, and
cook according to the package instructions
until tender but chewy. Drain the noodles,
reserving about ¼ cup/60 ml of the cooking
water. Rinse well to remove the surface starch
under cold running water until cooled, then
drain again very well.

Whisk together the tahini, vinegar, soy
sauce, ginger, the remaining 2 tsp of honey,
and the remaining 1 tsp of sesame oil in a
large bowl (you can use the same one the
squash was tossed in). Whisk in enough of
the reserved cooking water to thin the dressing,
usually about 2 tbsp.

Toss the noodles and kale in the dressing to
coat well. Pile the noodle mixture into four
bowls, dividing it evenly, then heap the
squash to one side. Lay an egg on top of each
noodle pile. Sprinkle with green onions and
togarashi. Just before serving, cut a slit in the
side of each egg to let the yolk flow.

to drink: *chilled sake*

egg tip: *The eggs can be cooked in the pot of boiling
water before the noodles.*

eGGs on LeFTovers

I've never met a cold slice of pizza that didn't taste better reheated with an egg on it. Actually, eggs reinvent most leftovers that are lurking in the fridge. Turn last night's pot roast into a morning hash. Hollow out that last half of a baked potato and pour in a scramble, or rewarm those decadent mashed potatoes and perch a poached egg in the middle, as the French would do.

As for Thanksgiving leftovers, the options are infinite: How about slipping a coddled egg into that turkey soup you make every year? Try frying up a hash of diced sweet potatoes and turkey and top it with an egg and sour cream. Spoon a helping of stuffing into a baking dish, add an egg, and bake until set, then drizzle the whole mess with hot gravy.

An egg spruces up just about any pasta dish; I can't think of one classic recipe on which they wouldn't be great. The same goes for cooked rice and whole grains. Leftover vegetables, soups, stir-fries, sandwiches, stews— nearly any kind of food is improved by the addition of an egg. Eggs have the power to transform the ho-hum into the yeehaw—just another reason why it really is the incredible, edible EGG.

index

a

Alsatian Cousin Pizza, 110
Anchovies
  Coastal Margherita Pizza, 107
  Grilled Romaine Caesar Salad with Eggs Mimosa, 137
  A Niçoise Salad, of Sorts, 144–45
Aromatic Lentils with Smoked Trout and Dilly Eggs, 182
Arugula
  A Niçoise Salad, of Sorts, 144–45
  Picnic Salad of Wheat Berries, Favas, Radishes, and
    Beet-Pickled Eggs, 143
  Steak and Eggs Salad, 146–47
  Whole-Wheat Spaghetti, Tuna, Chiles, Eggs, and
    Pangrattato, 191
Asparagus, Roasted, with Creamed Leeks, Morels, and
  Poppy Seed Eggs, 160
Avocados
  Broccolini, Avocado, and Pistachio Salad with Silky
    Lemon Dressing and Parsleyed Eggs, 138
  Crab Cakes Benny with Avocado Crema, 114–15
  A Working Girl's Supper of Crispy Lemon Eggs and
    Avocado on Toast, 92

B

Bacon
  Cardamom-Cornmeal Waffles with Eggs, Bacon, and
    Maple Syrup, 88
  Eggs Bourguignon (Oeufs en Meurette), 93–95
  Frisée aux Lardons and Crispy Breaded Eggs, 148
  Full English Breakfast Bowl, 185
  Nests of Carbonara, 188
  Summer Succotash with Creamy Simmered Eggs, 157
  Tomato, Bacon, and Egg Tartlets, 104
Baked Sweet Corn Polenta with Tomato Sauce and
  Eggs, 172
Basque Pipérade Beans with Baked Eggs, 184
Beans
  Basque Pipérade Beans with Baked Eggs, 184
  An Earthy Stew of Chickpeas and Swiss Chard with
    Crunchy Eggs, 127
  Full English Breakfast Bowl, 185
  A Niçoise Salad, of Sorts, 144–45
  Picnic Salad of Wheat Berries, Favas, Radishes, and
    Beet-Pickled Eggs, 143
  Summer Succotash with Creamy Simmered Eggs, 157
Bean sprouts
  Shrimp Pad Thai, 194–95
Beef
  Quail Egg Crostini Three Ways, 97–98

Red Flannel Hash with Fried Eggs and Horseradish
    Cream, 155–56
  Steak and Eggs Salad, 146–47
Beets
  Beet-Pickled Eggs, 80
  Picnic Salad of Wheat Berries, Favas, Radishes, and
    Beet-Pickled Eggs, 143
  Red Flannel Hash with Fried Eggs and Horseradish
    Cream, 155–56
Bell peppers
  Basque Pipérade Beans with Baked Eggs, 184
  Romesco Sauce, 162
  Shakshouka, 131
Bok Choy, Egg-Dropped Miso Soup with Mushrooms
  and, 122
Bouillabaisse of Eggs, 129–30
Bread
  Bouillabaisse of Eggs, 129–30
  Croque Mademoiselle, 102
  Eggs Baked on Crisped Bread and Kale Salad, 73
  Eggs Bourguignon (Oeufs en Meurette), 93–95
  Grilled Romaine Caesar Salad with Eggs Mimosa, 137
  Grilled Spring Onions with Hazelnut Romesco and
    Olive Oil Eggs, 162
  Quail Egg Crostini Three Ways, 97–98
  Spanish Garlic Soup with Poached Eggs and Pickled
    Grapes, 120–21
  Welsh Rarebit with Hide-and-Seek Eggs and Burnt
    Broccoli, 100–101
  A Working Girl's Supper of Crispy Lemon Eggs and
    Avocado on Toast, 92
Breaded Eggs, 67
Broccoli, Burnt, Welsh Rarebit with Hide-and-Seek Eggs
  and, 100–101
Broccolini, Avocado, and Pistachio Salad with Silky
  Lemon Dressing and Parsleyed Eggs, 138
Brussels sprouts
  Alsatian Cousin Pizza, 110
  Stir-Fried Brussels Sprouts and Wok-Fried Eggs, 165

c

Cabbage
  Duck Fried Rice with Kumquats and Lots of
    Veggies, 179–81
Caesar Salad, Grilled Romaine, with Eggs Mimosa, 137
Caramelized Onion Matzo Brei, 53
Cardamom-Cornmeal Waffles with Eggs, Bacon, and
  Maple Syrup, 88

Carrots
    Aromatic Lentils with Smoked Trout and Dilly
      Eggs, 182
    Duck Fried Rice with Kumquats and Lots of
      Veggies, 179–81
    Spicy and Herbaceous Thai Salad with Salted Duck
      Eggs, 142
    Spring Sorrel Soup with Tender Vegetables and
      Coddled Eggs, 124
Cauliflower
    Twenty Minutes Till Couscous, 170
Chalazae, 18
Charred Rapini with Garlic-Chile Eggs, 158
Cheddar Sauce, 100
Cheese
    Alsatian Cousin Pizza, 110
    Cheddar Sauce, 100
    Chilaquiles, 112–13
    Coastal Margherita Pizza, 107
    Croque Mademoiselle, 102
    Crushed Potatoes with Chorizo, Eggs, and Green
      Chile Salsa, 152–53
    Farrotto with Delicata Squash and Sage–Brown Butter
      Eggs, 175–77
    Forest Floor Pizza, 110
    Nests of Carbonara, 188
    Pig and Honey Pizza, 107
    Quail Egg Crostini Three Ways, 97–98
    Risi e Bisi, 178
    Shakshouka, 131
    Shells and Cheese with Caramelized Fennel and
      Crispy Breaded Eggs, 192–93
    Steak and Eggs Salad, 146–47
    Welsh Rarebit with Hide-and-Seek Eggs and Burnt
      Broccoli, 100–101
Chicken, Green Pozole with Fresh Corn, Eggs, and
    (Manterola's Pozolillo Verde), 118–19
Chickpeas, An Earthy Stew of Swiss Chard and, with
    Crunchy Eggs, 127
Chiles
    Chilaquiles, 112–13
    Egg Hoppers (Sri Lankan Crêpes) with Mint Sambal,
      89–91
    Green Chile Salsa, 153
    Romesco Sauce, 162
    Spicy Golden Eggs, 83
    Whole-Wheat Spaghetti, Tuna, Chiles, Eggs, and
      Pangrattato, 191
Chinese Tea Eggs, 34
Cholesterol, 15
Coastal Margherita Pizza, 107
Coddled Eggs, 31

Corn
    Baked Sweet Corn Polenta with Tomato Sauce and
      Eggs, 172
    Manterola's Pozolillo Verde (Green Pozole with
      Chicken, Fresh Corn, and Eggs), 118–19
    Summer Succotash with Creamy Simmered Eggs, 157
Cornmeal
    Baked Sweet Corn Polenta with Tomato Sauce and
      Eggs, 172
    Cardamom-Cornmeal Waffles with Eggs, Bacon, and
      Maple Syrup, 88
    Fried Green Tomato Salad with Softly Scrambled
      Eggs, 140
Couscous, Twenty Minutes Till, 170
Crab Cakes Benny with Avocado Crema, 114–15
Crispy Fried Eggs, 61
Croque Mademoiselle, 102
Crostini Three Ways, Quail Egg, 97–98
Crunchy Deep-Fried Eggs, 66
Crushed Potatoes with Chorizo, Eggs, and Green Chile
    Salsa, 152–53

D Duck eggs, 12
    Alsatian Cousin Pizza, 110
    baked, 69
    Bouillabaisse of Eggs, 129–30
    broiled, 69
    Coastal Margherita Pizza, 107
    Duck Fried Rice with Kumquats and Lots of
      Veggies, 179–81
    Forest Floor Pizza, 110
    pickled, 76
    Pig and Honey Pizza, 107
    poached, 37
    Quintessential Poached Eggs, 38–40
    salted, 76, 77
    scrambled, 46
    simmered, 27
    Spicy and Herbaceous Thai Salad with Salted Duck
      Eggs, 142
    Duck Fried Rice with Kumquats and Lots of
      Veggies, 179–81
    Dukkah, 71

e An Earthy Stew of Chickpeas and Swiss Chard with
    Crunchy Eggs, 127
    Egg-Dropped Miso Soup with Mushrooms and Bok
    Choy, 122
    Egg Hoppers (Sri Lankan Crêpes) with Mint Sambal,
    89–91
    Eggs. *See also individual recipes*
      baked and broiled, 68–74

eggs on top

coddled, 31
cracking, 12
doneness of yolks, 11, 14
freshness of, 13, 17–18
fried, 54–67
grades of, 13
grated, 30
kinds of, 12
labels for, 19–20
on leftovers, 202
nutrition of, 15, 20
parts of, 17–18
poached, 36–44
preserved, 76–83
safety of raw, 14
scrambled, 46–53
separating, 12
simmered ("boiled"), 24–25, 27–28
size of, 13
storing, 14
Eggs and Greens Masala, 125
Eggs Baked on Crisped Bread and Kale Salad, 73
Eggs Baked with Mushrooms, Thyme, and Cream, 72
Eggs Bourguignon (Oeufs en Meurette), 93–95
Eggs Flavorfully Basted, 60
Eggs in Purgatory, 74
8-Minute Eggs, 28

F Farrotto with Delicata Squash and Sage–Brown Butter
    Eggs, 175–77
Fennel
    Bouillabaisse of Eggs, 129–30
    Shells and Cheese with Caramelized Fennel and
        Crispy Breaded Eggs, 192–93
15-Minute Eggs, 28
Fish. See also Anchovies
    Aromatic Lentils with Smoked Trout and Dilly
        Eggs, 182
    A Niçoise Salad, of Sorts, 144–45
    Tuna Sauce, 144
    Whole-Wheat Spaghetti, Tuna, Chiles, Eggs, and
        Pangrattato, 191
5-Minute Eggs, 28
Foolproof Poached Eggs, 44
Forest Floor Pizza, 110
4-Minute Eggs, 27
Fried Green Tomato Salad with Softly Scrambled
    Eggs, 140
Frisée aux Lardons and Crispy Breaded Eggs, 148
Full English Breakfast Bowl, 185

G Garlic
    Garlic-Chile Eggs, 62
    Garlic-Scallion Noodles, 199
    Rouille, 130
    Spanish Garlic Soup with Poached Eggs and Pickled
        Grapes, 120–21
Goose eggs, 12
Grapes, Pickled, 121
Grated Eggs, 30
Green Chile Salsa, 153
Greens
    Eggs and Greens Masala, 125
    A Niçoise Salad, of Sorts, 144–45
Grilled Romaine Caesar Salad with Eggs Mimosa, 137
Grilled Spring Onions with Hazelnut Romesco and
    Olive Oil Eggs, 162–63

H Ham
    Basque Pipérade Beans with Baked Eggs, 184
    Croque Mademoiselle, 102
    Quail Egg Crostini Three Ways, 97–98
Hash, Red Flannel, with Fried Eggs and Horseradish
    Cream, 155–56

J Japanese Soy Sauce Eggs (Shoyu Tamago), 33

K Kale
    Eggs Baked on Crisped Bread and Kale Salad, 73
    Miso-Creamed Kale and Mushrooms with Soy Sauce
        Eggs, 166
    Soba Noodle Salad with Soft Eggs, Kale, and
        Kabocha, 200
Kimchi Ramen, 197–98
Kumquats, Duck Fried Rice with, and Lots of
    Veggies, 179–81

L Leeks
    Bouillabaisse of Eggs, 129–30
    Leeks Vinaigrette with Herbed Quail Eggs, 135
    Roasted Asparagus with Creamed Leeks, Morels, and
        Poppy Seed Eggs, 160
    Spanish Garlic Soup with Poached Eggs and Pickled
        Grapes, 120–21
    Spring Sorrel Soup with Tender Vegetables and
        Coddled Eggs, 124
Leftovers, eggs on, 202
Lentils, Aromatic, with Smoked Trout and Dilly
    Eggs, 182
Lettuce
    Grilled Romaine Caesar Salad with Eggs Mimosa, 137

Spicy and Herbaceous Thai Salad with Salted Duck Eggs, 142

M Manterola's Pozolillo Verde (Green Pozole with Chicken, Fresh Corn, and Eggs), 118–19
Masala, Eggs and Greens, 125
Matzo Brei, Caramelized Onion, 53
Milk-Poached Eggs, 42
Mint Sambal, 89
Miso
  Egg-Dropped Miso Soup with Mushrooms and Bok Choy, 122
  Miso-Creamed Kale and Mushrooms with Soy Sauce Eggs, 166
Mushrooms
  Egg-Dropped Miso Soup with Mushrooms and Bok Choy, 122
  Eggs Baked with Mushrooms, Thyme, and Cream, 72
  Eggs Bourguignon (Oeufs en Meurette), 93–95
  Forest Floor Pizza, 110
  Full English Breakfast Bowl, 185
  Miso-Creamed Kale and Mushrooms with Soy Sauce Eggs, 166
  Roasted Asparagus with Creamed Leeks, Morels, and Poppy Seed Eggs, 160

n Nests of Carbonara, 188
A Niçoise Salad, of Sorts, 144–45
9- to 12-Minute Eggs, 28
Noodles. *See* Pasta and noodles
Nutrition, 15, 20

o Oeufs en Meurette (Eggs Bourguignon), 93–95
Olives
  A Niçoise Salad, of Sorts, 144–45
  Twenty Minutes Till Couscous, 170
Omega-3 fatty acids, 20
Onions
  Caramelized Onion Matzo Brei, 53
  Grilled Spring Onions with Hazelnut Romesco and Olive Oil Eggs, 162–63
  Spicy Tomato Sauce with Onion and Butter, 74
Oven Eggs with Olive Oil and Dukkah, 71
Over Easy, 58
Over Hard, 58
Over Medium, 58

P Pad Thai, Shrimp, 194–95
Pancetta
  Risi e Bisi, 178

Panfried Eggs with Varying Degrees of Doneness, 56–58
Parsnips
  Spicy and Herbaceous Thai Salad with Salted Duck Eggs, 142
  Spring Sorrel Soup with Tender Vegetables and Coddled Eggs, 124
Pasta and noodles
  Garlic-Scallion Noodles, 199
  Kimchi Ramen, 197–98
  Nests of Carbonara, 188
  Shells and Cheese with Caramelized Fennel and Crispy Breaded Eggs, 192–93
  Shrimp Pad Thai, 194–95
  Soba Noodle Salad with Soft Eggs, Kale, and Kabocha, 200
  Whole-Wheat Spaghetti, Tuna, Chiles, Eggs, and Pangrattato, 191
Peas
  Nests of Carbonara, 188
  Risi e Bisi, 178
  Twenty Minutes Till Couscous, 170
Pickled Grapes, 121
Picnic Salad of Wheat Berries, Favas, Radishes, and Beet-Pickled Eggs, 143
Pig and Honey Pizza, 107
Pizzas
  Alsatian Cousin Pizza, 110
  Coastal Margherita Pizza, 107
  Forest Floor Pizza, 110
  Pig and Honey Pizza, 107
  Pizza of the Rising Sun, 105–6
  Pizza Sauce, 111
Poached Eggs for a Crowd, 40
Poached Scrambled Eggs, 52
Polenta, Baked Sweet Corn, with Tomato Sauce and Eggs, 172
Pork. *See also* Bacon; Ham; Pancetta; Sausage
  Kimchi Ramen, 197–98
Potatoes
  Bouillabaisse of Eggs, 129–30
  Crushed Potatoes with Chorizo, Eggs, and Green Chile Salsa, 152–53
  A Niçoise Salad, of Sorts, 144–45
  Red Flannel Hash with Fried Eggs and Horseradish Cream, 155–56
  Spring Sorrel Soup with Tender Vegetables and Coddled Eggs, 124
Pozolillo Verde, Manterola's (Green Pozole with Chicken, Fresh Corn, and Eggs), 118–19
Puff pastry
  Tomato, Bacon, and Egg Tartlets, 104

Q Quail eggs, 12
  Alsatian Cousin Pizza, 110
  Coastal Margherita Pizza, 107
  Forest Floor Pizza, 110
  fried, 57
  Leeks Vinaigrette with Herbed Quail Eggs, 135
  pickled, 76
  Pig and Honey Pizza, 107
  poached, 37
  Quail Egg Crostini Three Ways, 97–98
  simmered, 27
Quintessential Poached Eggs, 38–40

R Radishes
  Aromatic Lentils with Smoked Trout and Dilly
    Eggs, 182
  Picnic Salad of Wheat Berries, Favas, Radishes, and
    Beet-Pickled Eggs, 143
Rapini, Charred, with Garlic-Chile Eggs, 158
Red Flannel Hash with Fried Eggs and Horseradish
  Cream, 155–56
Rice
  Duck Fried Rice with Kumquats and Lots of
    Veggies, 179–81
  Miso-Creamed Kale and Mushrooms with Soy Sauce
    Eggs, 166
  Risi e Bisi, 178
Roasted Asparagus with Creamed Leeks, Morels, and
  Poppy Seed Eggs, 160
Romesco Sauce, 162
Rouille, 130

S Sage–Brown Butter Eggs, 62
Salads
  Broccolini, Avocado, and Pistachio Salad with Silky
    Lemon Dressing and Parsleyed Eggs, 138
  Eggs Baked on Crisped Bread and Kale Salad, 73
  Fried Green Tomato Salad with Softly Scrambled
    Eggs, 140
  Frisée aux Lardons and Crispy Breaded Eggs, 148
  Grilled Romaine Caesar Salad with Eggs Mimosa, 137
  Leeks Vinaigrette with Herbed Quail Eggs, 135
  A Niçoise Salad, of Sorts, 144–45
  Picnic Salad of Wheat Berries, Favas, Radishes, and
    Beet-Pickled Eggs, 143
  Soba Noodle Salad with Soft Eggs, Kale, and
    Kabocha, 200
  Spicy and Herbaceous Thai Salad with Salted Duck
    Eggs, 142
  Steak and Eggs Salad, 146–47
Salmonella, 14
Salsas. *See* Sauces

Salted Eggs, 76, 77
Sandwiches
  Croque Mademoiselle, 102
Sauces
  Cheddar Sauce, 100
  Green Chile Salsa, 153
  Pizza Sauce, 111
  Romesco Sauce, 162
  Rouille, 130
  Salsa Verde, 97, 98
  Spicy Tomato Sauce with Onion and Butter, 74
  Tuna Sauce, 144
Sausage
  Crushed Potatoes with Chorizo, Eggs, and Green
    Chile Salsa, 152–53
  Pig and Honey Pizza, 107
Scrambled Eggs, Two Ways, 49–50
7-Minute Eggs, 28
Shakshouka, 131
Shells and Cheese with Caramelized Fennel and Crispy
  Breaded Eggs, 192–93
Shoyu Tamago (Japanese Soy Sauce Eggs), 33
Shrimp
  Egg Hoppers (Sri Lankan Crêpes) with Mint Sambal,
    89–91
  Shrimp Pad Thai, 194–95
Simmered Eggs, 27–28
6-Minute Eggs, 28
Soba Noodle Salad with Soft Eggs, Kale, and
  Kabocha, 200
Sorrel Soup, Spring, with Tender Vegetables and
  Coddled Eggs, 124
Soups
  Egg-Dropped Miso Soup with Mushrooms and Bok
    Choy, 122
  Manterola's Pozolillo Verde (Green Pozole with
    Chicken, Fresh Corn, and Eggs), 118–19
  Spanish Garlic Soup with Poached Eggs and Pickled
    Grapes, 120–21
  Spring Sorrel Soup with Tender Vegetables and
    Coddled Eggs, 124
Soy Sauce Eggs, Japanese (Shoyu Tamago), 33
Spanish Garlic Soup with Poached Eggs and Pickled
  Grapes, 120–21
Spicy and Herbaceous Thai Salad with Salted Duck
  Eggs, 142
Spicy Golden Eggs, 83
Spicy Tomato Sauce with Onion and Butter, 74
Spinach
  A Niçoise Salad, of Sorts, 144–45
  Spring Sorrel Soup with Tender Vegetables and
    Coddled Eggs, 124

Whole-Wheat Spaghetti, Tuna, Chiles, Eggs, and
Pangrattato, 191
Spring Sorrel Soup with Tender Vegetables and Coddled
Eggs, 124
Squash
Farrotto with Delicata Squash and Sage–Brown Butter
Eggs, 175–77
Soba Noodle Salad with Soft Eggs, Kale, and
Kabocha, 200
Summer Succotash with Creamy Simmered Eggs, 157
Steak and Eggs Salad, 146–47
Stir-Fried Brussels Sprouts and Wok-Fried Eggs, 165
Succotash, Summer, with Creamy Simmered Eggs, 157
Sunny-Side Up Eggs, 56
Sunny-Side Up from the Oven, 56
Sweet potatoes
Red Flannel Hash with Fried Eggs and Horseradish
Cream, 155–56
Swiss Chard, An Earthy Stew of Chickpeas and, with
Crunchy Eggs, 127

T Tartlets, Tomato, Bacon, and Egg, 104
Tea Eggs, Chinese, 34
13-Minute Eggs, 28
3-Minute Eggs, 27
Tofu
Egg-Dropped Miso Soup with Mushrooms and Bok
Choy, 122
Shrimp Pad Thai, 194–95
Tomatillos
Green Chile Salsa, 153
Manterola's Pozolillo Verde (Green Pozole with
Chicken, Fresh Corn, and Eggs), 118–19
Tomatoes
Baked Sweet Corn Polenta with Tomato Sauce and
Eggs, 172
Basque Pipérade Beans with Baked Eggs, 184
Bouillabaisse of Eggs, 129–30
Chilaquiles, 112–13
Eggs and Greens Masala, 125
Eggs in Purgatory, 74
Fried Green Tomato Salad with Softly Scrambled
Eggs, 140
Full English Breakfast Bowl, 185
A Niçoise Salad, of Sorts, 144–45
Pizza Sauce, 111
Quail Egg Crostini Three Ways, 97–98

Romesco Sauce, 162
Shakshouka, 131
Spicy Tomato Sauce with Onion and Butter, 74
Tomato, Bacon, and Egg Tartlets, 104
Twenty Minutes Till Couscous, 170
Tortillas
Chilaquiles, 112–13
Manterola's Pozolillo Verde (Green Pozole with
Chicken, Fresh Corn, and Eggs), 118–19
Trout, Smoked, Aromatic Lentils with Dilly Eggs
and, 182
Tuna
A Niçoise Salad, of Sorts, 144–45
Tuna Sauce, 144
Whole-Wheat Spaghetti, Tuna, Chiles, Eggs, and
Pangrattato, 191
Turkey eggs, 12
Turnips
Aromatic Lentils with Smoked Trout and Dilly
Eggs, 182
Twenty Minutes Till Couscous, 170

V Vegetables. *See also individual vegetables*
Duck Fried Rice with Kumquats and Lots of
Veggies, 179–81
Spring Sorrel Soup with Tender Vegetables and
Coddled Eggs, 124
Vitamin E, 20

W Waffles, Cardamom-Cornmeal, with Eggs, Bacon, and
Maple Syrup, 88
Welsh Rarebit with Hide-and-Seek Eggs and Burnt
Broccoli, 100–101
Wheat Berries, Picnic Salad of Favas, Radishes,
Beet-Pickled Eggs, and, 143
Whole-Wheat Spaghetti, Tuna, Chiles, Eggs, and
Pangrattato, 191
Wine
Eggs Bourguignon (Oeufs en Meurette), 93–95
Wine-Poached Eggs, 41
Wok-Fried Eggs, 64
A Working Girl's Supper of Crispy Lemon Eggs and
Avocado on Toast, 92

Z Zucchini
Summer Succotash with Creamy Simmered Eggs, 157